VICAR'S WIFE C

Other books by Jane Grayshon
  A Pathway through Pain (Kingsway)
  In Times of Pain (Lion)
  Faith in Flames (Hodder & Stoughton)
  Confessions of a Vicar's Wife (Monarch)

Vicar's Wife on the Move!

JANE GRAYSHON

MITRE
Tunbridge Wells

British Library Cataloguing in Publication Data
A catalogue record for this book is available
from the British Library.

ISBN: 1 85424 223 7

Produced by Bookprint Creative Services,
P.O. Box 827, BN23 6NX, England for
Mitre, an imprint of Monarch Publications
P.O. Box 163, Tunbridge Wells, Kent TN3 0NZ
Printed in England by Clays Ltd, St Ives plc

March 1992

March 1992

Friday 20 March

7 am Woke excited. Today is publication day of *Confessions of a Vicar's Wife*.

Went through the day several times in my head. Appointment at the hairdresser—a treat, but tinged with guilt at the extravagance of it on a clergyman's stipend. Visit from newspaper reporter and photographer—excitement or tedium? Probably both. Drive to Radio Merseyside studios to record my weekly 'slot' for Sunday's programme—definitely fun. Dash home in time to meet children out of school—in time to be pulled back to earth, back from any grandiose ideas of the glamour of the day. Roll sleeves up for the cook/bottle-wash/listen to children reading before the evening.

. . . This evening. I hugged my knees in a childlike burst of excitement. This evening was the big 'do': the launch of my book in Liverpool Cathedral. Several hundred tickets sold, the organiser had said, to people from all over the Merseyside area. Many of them are listeners to my local radio series of *Confessions*, which was, after all, where this book had begun.

Mostly, I felt excited, though I was also nervous. Nervous and daunted. I dreaded being a disappointment. Matthew had told me that was ridiculous.

'Don't be silly!' he'd said. 'Entertaining an audience for two hours is a great opportunity!' Then he'd added, 'I do it every Sunday!'

I'd replied, with a distinct glower, that it was OK for him; he had the structure of a Church of England service to guide him through his two hours. Mine was a free programme which could as easily be a flop as it could be fun.

Matthew had observed with a sigh, 'The artistic temperament is truly neurotic!' But at least he had accompanied his comment with a nice kiss.

I lay in bed and watched Matthew sleep on. It was nice to know I've one fan, no matter how much of a flop tonight is.

9 am Hairdresser said, 'Are you doing anything special tonight?'

I replied, 'I'm speaking in Liverpool Cathedral.'

Shocked look.

'Are you a nun, then?'

'Not quite.'

Decided it was a good idea to give her the impression I enjoy silence.

11 am Newspaper reporter came. Asked various questions for her article: What was it like being a vicar's wife? Or an author, for that matter? And why had I chosen to write about pain, of all things?

Explained that I'd been seriously ill on and off for several years after peritonitis. Tried to reflect as wisely as I could on life, and death, commenting how hard it is to see God at such times, yet that we get occasional glimpses. Every time I did so she put her pen down, listened hard, and said in her Liverpool accent, 'Yeah, that's dead true, that!'

Then she'd pick up her pen and continue, 'Now, where were we?'

She didn't consider writing one single word about important issues for her newspaper article.

Most frustrating. And definitely more tedium than glamour.

5 pm In middle of harassed mother syndrome, the doorbell rang. It was my publisher, Henry, who had taken the train all the way from Kent. He stood on the doorstep with an enormous, floppy-leafed plant. Both he and it looked rather travel-weary.

Enthusiastic, elated greetings. Matthew pulled the cork on the first wine bottle of the evening. I wondered, not for the first time, why an author–publisher relationship is so emotionally charged.

Evening I babbled nervously (and, probably, ridiculously) to Matthew and Henry all the way to Liverpool Cathedral. Arrived to find posters hanging from trestle tables, stacked with attractively laid-out piles of the freshly printed book. The whole entrance adorned with large photos of myself.

Thought, This is ME!

Tried to look composed, as if I could take it all in my stride. Was inordinately grateful for Matthew's almost physical support at my side.

Survived being up on stage and, happily, so did the audience. My adrenalin was flowing very helpfully.

First time my anxiety was justified was during the interval when I came down to sign books. Members of the audience kept referring—jovially—to one question. Would this book ruin my husband's career?

Little did they know how pertinent a question this was.

Matthew replied on my behalf every time. 'It's terrible being her husband!' he complained with a twinkle. 'I think I'd better find a job somewhere else now that her *Confessions* are published.'

He conveyed a roguish grin in my direction.

I nearly dropped my pen in horror. Because the point was, Matthew was indeed seeking to do exactly that: find a job elsewhere. But, since the matter was supposed to be entirely confidential, we could not say. Not even give a hint.

This 'joke' was very much too near the bone!

They laughed. To my dismay, this led Matthew to embellish his idea.

'Perhaps I'd better go to a distant diocese . . . ' he continued with an innocent-looking smile, as if this idea had just come to him in a moment of spontaneous inspiration. 'Somewhere far away, out of range from the airwaves of Radio Merseyside, where people haven't heard my wife's tales about me!'

He looked across to me. I wished the floor would open up and swallow me. Because we *were* waiting to hear about a job in another 'distant diocese': in a town east of Penzance, actually. Every day for the last week or so we'd been expecting a letter in the post, telling us the outcome of Matthew's application.

'At least I'd be out of range of all you listeners!' he joked.

They laughed again. Raucously.

I laughed too. Nobody noticed that my high-pitched cackle was not so much mirth as desperation.

I could have strangled Matthew.

Fortunately for him, I had to get back on stage instead, for part two of my talk.

More informal chat with people at the end of the evening. This time the oft-repeated question was, Would I be writing a sequel? And if so, what title would I choose?

I suggested with a grin that I'd probably call it, *It Shouldn't Happen to a Vicar's Wife*. Because an awful lot of what happens to me shouldn't, I'm sure.

Made the briefest allusion to the fact that a midwife who has worked in an infertility clinic does know quite a bit more about the facts of life than most people assume of a vicar's wife. She *does* know where babies come from, and how; she *has* heard swear words (and could probably teach a few choice phrases—women in labour display an astonishing vocabulary).

The conversation widened to general speculation on possible titles. What about *Vicar's Wife in a Spin*? Certainly, that would be a pretty accurate description.

Matthew turned the conversation. He suggested *he* could write the sequel.

'Oh yes?' They were intrigued.

Oh yes, he said. He could call it, *Vicar In Harness*. As he spoke these words he gave a very knowing jerk of the head towards me; a 'Life-Is-Very-Hard-For-Husbands' look.

Much laughter. Except from me.

I found myself thinking of the title of another book: *Murder in the Cathedral*.

Saturday 21 March

Matthew's day off. Phone rang very early, when we were still in bed. I groaned at the invasion of parish life into our bed, even. Let Sleeping Vicars Lie, I thought at the phone, remembering last night's book titles.

Matthew picked up the receiver.

I couldn't hear who it was, but I could deduce that it must have been someone important, because Matthew put on his 'I've Been To Public School Too, Chaps!' voice.

Was this phone call about his new job application?

All resentment about the ridiculous time of the

phone call, on Matthew's day off, suddenly melted. I wanted to overhear and savour every nuance.

'Er, yes ... ' Matthew smiled. 'I AM Matthew Grayshon.'

Pause.

'That's an interesting question' he said. Broad smile. 'Shall we say, yes, I AM the vicar here ...'

It had to be them!

'At least, I am until next week ...'

Pause again. Clearly, whoever was at the other end of the line was as mystified as I was. It sounded as if he had another job already lined up to begin next week.

'What I mean is that, now my wife's book of *Confessions* is published, I may not last as vicar for much longer!'

Matthew's face became animated, and he fixed his eyes on me, as if I must be the subject under discussion. He covered the receiver and whispered, 'Editor of the *Church Times*.'

Immediate disappointment over Matthew's job, balanced by a surge of excitement. Especially when, a moment later, Matthew whispered again, 'Wants to run an extract.'

Sounded good!

Not a lengthy call. The editor had simply wanted to clarify facts about Matthew's position, for the introduction to the extract.

It had served to pose a most pertinent question. Could a vicar's job prospects be jeopardised if his wife is a bit untraditional?

More specifically, will Matthew get the job he fancies, despite having a wife like *me*?

Monday 23 March

Fed up waiting for the letter about Matthew's latest application.

Told myself he probably won't be shortlisted anyway. The church sounds the best kind of place we would enjoy. Just 'him' spiritually, in a town which sounds just 'us' socially.

Does God give us the best when we want it?

Whether Matthew gets this job or not, all I want is to KNOW!

Tuesday 24 March

Still no post. Except bills.

Phone call from the Rev William Charles Waldegrove-Smythe, a priest in a nearby parish in Runcorn. He's a man whom we and others tease quite mercilessly for being an aspiring Somebody in the church hierarchy. He's a man of stature—not just physically—who must be incredibly important if importance is measured according to the width of one's briefcase.

William Charles was writing a news column for his parish magazine and he believed that I'd written a new book which would be of interest to his parishioners. Did he have my permission to write a short piece about the 'local author'?

Yes.

He asked me the title.

All fears that *Confessions of a Vicar's Wife* might sound like a smutty book rushed round my mind. I wished, for a moment, that I'd chosen a quiet, obsequious title, because there's no way of making this one sound dignified. Not even with my best, most polite voice. And there's something about the Rev William Charles Waldegrove-Smythe which invariably causes me to speak to him using my best voice. Perhaps I feel as if that makes me sound more like 'his type'.

Anyway, he had asked me the title and I could not avoid telling him. I did so, solemnly.

The telephone line went very quiet.

At last, tentatively, I asked, 'Are you still there?'

The Rev William Charles Waldegrove-Smythe cleared his throat.

'I'm writing,' he replied.

Rev William Charles Waldegrove-Smythe is a somewhat formal high churchman. I think he may regard me with some suspicion.

Wednesday 25 March

Letter postmarked with the name of the town east of Penzance.

After so long waiting, it was as if we could not bear to open it. We both examined the envelope thoroughly several times. Scrutinised the typeface on the address: yes, that parish obviously uses a computer. Wonder if this means they have a secretary? That would be good.

Above our address was written, *Confidential*. Matthew gave a rather derisory snort.

'They're assuming my mail is opened by a parish secretary,' he commented. 'I do hope they're not so well-endowed that they've forgotten that most churches struggle along with far less than they can imagine!'

He sounded as if he was trying to find something bad to say about them; as if he needed to convince himself that he wouldn't fancy going there, so he wouldn't mind if they hadn't shortlisted him.

'Aren't you going to open it then?'

He rummaged around for ages looking for the right knife to slit it open.

His face gave away nothing as he read.

Then he looked up.

'They've shortlisted me,' he announced.

I am not one to restrain my spontaneity.

'YIPPEE!' I hooted.

Matthew passed me the letter. Interviews in one month, but candidates were 'warmly invited' to visit the parish before then to see around and get a 'feel' of the place, meeting folk from the church. Expenses paid, accommodation provided, any queries answered. It sounded wonderful.

Had a spring to my step all day.

Met several parishioners, all of whom commented on how nice it was to see how happy I am here in Runcorn. Mingled guilt and exhilaration.

Thursday 26 March

Matthew phoned the warden of the new parish to fix up our visit. Came through to the kitchen afterwards positively glowing.

'He sounded really nice,' he said.

Poured me a sherry. Clearly, he wanted to celebrate.

'Sounds as if it'd be a brilliant church for us to become a part of, you know.'

He told me the arrangements for us to go down in a fortnight.

'Which just leaves the references. They want three. I reckon that William Charles might be a good name to drop. D'you agree?'

I froze. I hadn't told Matthew about Rev Waldegrove-Smythe's phone call to me on Tuesday.

What if I've caused disapproval from Those On High in the Church of England, and ruined Matthew's chances of getting this job?

Friday 27 March

Woken by telephone ringing at 7 am. More thoughts of *Let Sleeping Vicars Lie*.

Muttered, 'And some people think vicars only work on Sundays!'

It was the Runcorn police. One of the churches, Beersheba, had been broken into again: windows smashed, ink squirted all over the vestry. Could Matthew come?

Matthew groaned as he dressed. 'More broken windows to replace,' he sighed. He did that, too. The church couldn't afford to pay a glazier.

'Never mind,' I reassured him. 'Once you've replaced them all with unbreakable glass that'll be the end of it.'

Matthew smiled weakly. He was weary of the sort of mindless vandalism which these attacks represented: the oppressive antagonism which seemed constantly to be chiselling away at the church.

'Anyway,' I tried again to soothe him. 'We probably won't be here for much longer.'

I beamed as I allowed thoughts of the future awaiting us—possibly—to replace the drudgery of this sort of day. Silently prayed for God to lead us through the open door into the parish east of Penzance.

Saturday 28 March

Matthew out all day again, replacing the windows he'd boarded up yesterday.

Was helped by one keen and kind parishioner, Ken, who was pleased with his observation that when anyone works alongside a priest, 'It must be called co-ordination.'

Matthew's voice was still dispirited when he returned home for tea.

'Must write to theological college,' he said, 'and tell them their syllabus for training vicars should include instruction on how to glaze windows.'

Sunday 29 March

In church sang,

> *'Broken for me*
> *Broken for you . . .'*

Had to suppress my giggles. After all, most people didn't know the church windows had been broken. They could see for themselves, all the windows were perfectly OK this week. Most people don't know the half of what a vicar does.

April

April

Monday 6 April

Unsure what to wear to visit this prospective parish.
Anything but look like a frumpy vicar's wife.
  Perhaps I should go for my mini-skirt?

Tuesday 7 April

Remembered that I mustn't offend. This was Matthew's job at stake. Decided—very reluctantly —that the mini-skirt might be a bit over the top.

Wondered about a dress. That looks good. Pulled it out of the wardrobe but, the moment I set my eyes on it, the vision returned to me of an occasion two years ago.* In the middle of a conversation with Henry, I'd dropped a peanut and it had disappeared straight down my front. Got stuck in . . . in the wrong place. I've never been able to wear that dress with an easy mind since.

Wednesday 8 April

A dress looks as if I'm trying to look smart. That would never do. Don't want to look too keen.

I should definitely go for a more casual approach. Jeans?

Thursday 9 April

No. Not jeans. Not for a formal visit. As my (extended) family would say, they're NQOCD.†

Decided to hold on to the idea of looking casual. Look as if I'd just thrown on the nearest skirt and jumper without even thinking about it.

Must give a lot of thought as to which skirt and jumper look most stunning.

Friday 10 April

Meal with Pete and Jo in Chester. Jo was wearing a skirt in the exact colours I want for Sunday. Admired it effusively.

* see *Confessions of a Vicar's Wife*, page 136
† NQOCD: Not Quite Our Class, Dahling

Then asked if I could borrow it next week.

She said yes!

Back home, I practised in front of my mirror getting the dismissive tone exactly correct when saying, 'Oh!' (toss of head). 'You think I look nice? In *this* old skirt and jumper?'

Saturday 11 April

It's tomorrow! Full of anticipation.

We're to leave straight after morning service. Reminded self I don't want to look too good in our own church with Jo's newly-ironed skirt, in case I arouse suspicion. How would I reply if anyone asked where we were going?

'Ah, didn't you know we're thinking of abandoning you? Our hearts are now set on another church . . .'

Rather hurtful to the present congregation. I didn't want to hurt those to whom I felt I belonged as a Christian. And we might not even be going to move.

Sunday 12 April

Drove rather faster than one ought down the motorways. Made it to the church warden's house just in time for the evening service.

Arranged to go into church anonymously, as if we were good friends staying with the warden and his wife. Neither of us wanted the attention we'd get as 'Prospective New Vicar And Wife Spying Out The Land.'

Packed church. Great service. I felt very much at ease. During the prayers everyone prayed for the 'new vicar' and I felt strangely warmed.

Was sure this was God telling me this was IT.

At the end of the service we stayed for coffee at the

back of the church. Wanted to get a feel of the place as detached observers.

Unfortunately, at least five couples made a bee line for me.

'Aren't you Jane Grayshon?' they asked eagerly. 'We've just watched a video about you in our home-group!'

Warden's wife blushed. 'Sorry,' she admitted. 'I didn't like to warn you you'd be recognised.'

Hopes for anonymity dwindled fast as the questions piled up.

'Why are you here?' they smiled. 'Are you very good friends with the warden, for you to be staying for the weekend?'

The more I hedged, the more quickly they began to cotton on.

'Wait a minute . . . your husband's a vicar, isn't he?'

Eyebrows rising. One could see the penny dropping. 'Is he here—*looking*?' Knowing wink with that word. 'Looking—to come here as vicar?'

One man pulled Matthew aside. Rather seriously he asked, 'What's it like being married to someone famous?'

I thought, uncharitably, Silly moo. Did he want Matthew to say that I pick my nose when nobody's looking, or something?

Matthew did not rise to the bait. In fact, he drew himself up to his full stature and replied, 'I think you should ask my wife that question!'

Decided it was impossible to view a church anonymously. Everyone always sniffs out a prospective vicar.

Or his wife.

Back to the warden's home later. We flopped in and were offered drinks.

Matthew's face lit up.

'Coffee?'

His face fell.

'Or wine?'

They were soon forgetting to stand on ceremony. Spent a super evening chatting, drinking wine, listening to one another, laughing.

Discussed plans for the interviews in another fortnight. There were four shortlisted candidates. Each would have two interviews: one with the two church representatives, and one with the Bishop, Archdeacon and Rural Dean together.

Everyone was to have lunch together. I was told that wives would be welcome to join in with as much of the day as they chose.

'That's very kind,' I said. 'Is there therefore an expectation for vicars' wives to come to these interviews, then?'

The warden sighed. 'Quite honestly, we don't know what to expect from clergy wives nowadays. Some are offended at being asked to come: others are offended at not being.'

I sensed that the changing role of women causes much more bewilderment than is articulated.

In bed I said to Matthew, 'I could happily live here with these people. I like it.'

Matthew agreed. 'It's nice,' he said.

But there was a slightly non-committal edge to his manner which I chose to ignore. Went to sleep hopeful, content in my conviction that God was guiding our every step.

Monday 13 April

At the sight of the delicious cooked breakfast I realised that this new parish was trying to impress us as much as we were trying to impress them.

Felt sufficiently at ease to point this out. We all laughed at ourselves and relaxed a bit more together.

Clearly, the warden and his wife had been discussing us since last evening. They seemed very positive towards us. They made several Freudian slips, like 'When you come—oh, er, I mean *if* . . .'

We were driven around the town to see the parish. All very pleasant. Excellent schools, within easy reach of the vicarage. Gradually more details about daily life fitted into place until I could imagine living here.

For lunch, a few other members of the church joined us. Lively conversation which was fun, although inevitably it came close to being an interview. What did Matthew think about x,y,z? What would he do if a,b,c?

I kept quiet. Generally behaved myself. Only because it was easier to observe the dynamics than if I'd been involved. And I enjoyed watching the silent nods of approval across the table as Matthew spoke.

My spirits rose higher and higher as the day drew on.

Just before we left for home, we asked to see round the vicarage. All part of envisaging our new home.

The church warden accompanying us remained downstairs while Matthew and I toured the rest of the house. It was the first time we'd been alone together since breakfast.

'YUK!' declared Matthew.

I knew he was referring to the rather institutional feel of the house.

'Never mind!' I said airily. 'We can soon use a bit of flair and perk this up.'

Matthew was poking at the flaking paintwork of one window-frame, and revealed the wood beneath to be completely rotten.

'No,' he said with a finality which eroded my confidence. He gestured towards the pub oppo-site where teenagers hung around aimlessly, kicking Coke cans. 'This place might look OK on the surface but underneath I suspect its pleasantness would wear off quickly.' He shook his head. 'This isn't the right place. That's all there is to it.'

I could not—would not—believe my ears.

'But—!' I began.

For several minutes in the empty house, while the warden waited patiently below, our debate went to and fro. Every reason Matthew gave for not coming I described as an excuse; each one I countered with my reasons. It seemed like deadlock. We found no middle way.

We descended the stairs. It was time to leave.

The warden was warm in his farewells, reflecting exactly my own feelings.

'Thank you for coming,' he said, squeezing Matthew's hand and mine. 'It's been a blessed 24 hours. We look forward to seeing you at the interviews . . . well, who knows what's ahead?' He smiled. 'We'll be praying for you very specially.'

He gave a wink which expressed the same hope I had had until only a few moments beforehand.

We drove off.

I began again, 'Matthew, I think you've got it wrong.'

Matthew sounded open-minded. 'I might have,' he agreed. 'But we'll wait until tomorrow to discover our distilled responses.'

He was soon asleep. I envied the male ability to switch off, while my female mind chewed and churned around every detail of the past 24 hours.

Very confused. Decided God wanted us there and Matthew was being too choosy picking faults. Was he looking for the perfect parish or something?

As if such a place existed!

Tuesday 14 April

Couldn't wait to get the children to school. I was more than ready to get stuck back into our debate.

The moment the front door had slammed shut behind them we sat down opposite one another.

I laid my trump card on the table. 'I'm sure that's the right place for us, you know.'

Itemised exactly why. Matthew listened carefully.

'I don't think so,' he said calmly. Sickeningly calmly.

So! It was his word against mine! I was prepared to roll up my sleeves and fight my corner.

Except, how could I? This wasn't our own opinions to fight over. It was God's will we were seeking. I felt constrained to bow to Matthew's priestly discernment.

Matthew took my hand and said, 'Lady, I simply didn't feel God calling me to that church. I enjoyed the Sunday service but had no stirring within. I could do the job, yes, but that would be all I'd be doing. A job. No inspiration. No overwhelming desire to lead them. Nothing.'

He put his arms round me. 'Just a horrid house,' he grinned.

I opened my mouth to tell him how easily I could make the house a lovely home; how it would be worth it because I would be happy there, and the children would, and that God sometimes asks people to sacrifice material niceties like a house in order to serve Him where He chooses.

But Matthew had put his finger over my lips.

'God didn't call me,' he said with a loving smile.

End of discussion.

Our big hug did not melt all my turmoil of doubt. What I didn't know was whether my intense frustration was with Matthew, or with God Himself.

Because it seemed as if God *doesn't* give us the good things we want.

Wednesday 15 April

Matthew wrote to both the church warden and the Bishop of the new parish, indicating that he no longer wished to be considered for the job.

Showed me the letter. My whole body felt like lead. Even the taste in my mouth was of metal.

It seemed so terribly final.

Spent most of the day tearful; torn between frustration and a sense of loss.

It was as if I'd begun to get excited about having a new baby, only to be told that it had all been a false hope.

Evening Had to do something to distract myself. Chose to join in with an aerobics class at the Community Centre. I'd work out my angst.

On way in, overheard two older ladies comment loudly at the indignity of the vicar's wife wearing a leotard and lycra leggings. They knew other people did nowadays but Oh! Fancy the Vicar's Wife!

Thursday 16 April

Matthew spent the morning sorting out a large order of stationery for the church office. I distinctly overheard him swear at one point. Gathered that he did not feel this was good use of a vicar's time; that he hadn't done four years' training at theological college for this; that if only our church could afford a secretary it would make a big difference.

I came through and offered to help. He muttered vague thanks through his gritted teeth. Said I could collect his order from the shop if I liked.

'If I liked'!

Blinking cheek!

For selfish reasons, I decided to go. Knew I'd have a more pleasant husband if I went out of my way for him. Wanted a pleasant husband.

Arrived at the shop and asked for the goods. The assistant said immediately, 'You've come for Mr Grayshon? Ah, he's ever so nice, isn't he, Doreen?'

Doreen, from the back of the shop, stopped stacking her shelf to say, 'Ah, yeah, we think 'e's great.'

I didn't offer my current opinion of him. In any case, they weren't asking me; simply agreeing with one another as if in a scripted dialogue.

'Yeah, 'e is. Especially for a vicar, eh, Doreen?'

Doreen was nodding her agreement.

'Especially for a vicar,' she said solemnly. 'Yeah. Or a minister.'

'That's right, yeah. I mean, they're usually so miserable, aren't they, them lot.'

'Miserable!' echoed Doreen.

I smiled to myself at the thought of so many, so stereotyped vicars: men like the one I'd met only a few weeks ago after a funeral, standing with his overlarge greatcoat drooping about his shoulders, with a gormless drip hanging at the end of his nose for an inordinate length of time before he had wiped it with his greying handkerchief. How *do* vicars manage to look like this? Matthew had commented that this particular clergyman looked ripe to be made Canon.

'But not Mr Grayshon,' the two assistants' dialogue was continuing. 'Ah, 'e's lovely.' They were positively cooing.

'Yeah, and such fun. 'e always gives us a laugh.'

Then suddenly it was as if Doreen came out of her script.

''ere, watch it,' she warned. 'That might be 'is wife you're speaking to!'

I allowed myself to smile outwardly. And it was as if that first condescending smile cracked my stiff face. Their babble had soothed my irritation and I was warmed. Soon we were all laughing.

I drove home with a second, selfish reason for being glad I'd gone on that errand for Matthew. I'd been reminded how thankful I am that my husband has neither an ill-fitting greatcoat, nor a permanent drip at the end of his nose.

Friday 17 April

We're back to the Friday routine: Matthew scouring the job adverts in the church newspapers to see what's going. I wondered how many other vicars have a similar routine to Matthew's?

It's almost a ritual. He pedals home from the newsagent and sits straight down with a cup of coffee to read his *Church Times*. Front page first, inside back page, then Situations Vacant.

He sits there pawing his way down the list and giving what he might call a running commentary. This consists almost entirely of monosyllables:

'Ner' (short for No).

'Ner.'

'Ner.'

Then he reads the Deaths column and says, 'Gosh, I wouldn't fancy HIS parish.'

Evening Phone call from Jo. Hoped we'd had chicken pox, because Zachary's just come out in spots. Thus he must have been highly infectious last Friday when we saw him.

He was very sorry for himself.

Saturday 18 April

Decided to visit Zachary who is, after all, godson as well as nephew.

He was feeling much better. Was thrilled to see us and show off his spots.

'I've got chicken pox because I'm small,' he said.

I hesitated to disagree with his two-year-old logic.

He explained patiently, 'When I'm a bigger boy, I'll have cockerel pox!'

Sunday 19 April

Found it extremely odd and uncomfortable that I couldn't say anything to anyone in church about what the future might hold. It's considered 'very bad form' to give even a hint.

Apparently the principle is that, once it's known that a vicar's looking for a move, parishioners tend to feel greatly unsettled. They could start considering him to have abandoned his love for them, yet he could still be with them for another couple of years.

But these people in church happen to be my friends! I felt as if I had to hide the real me in order to bow to parishioners' needs.

This does NOT come naturally.

Monday 20 April

No idea what'll happen next. I suppose it's back to the drawing board now. Back to wondering where on earth we should go to next, or indeed if God intends Matthew to move at all from Runcorn in the near future.

To think, this has been going on for about a year! Very unsettling, no matter how happy one feels in the parish itself.

Maybe the Bishop will suggest somewhere. Or the Archdeacon, or someone else in the hierarchy of the Church of England. One is approached. ('Matthew, we're wondering if you would consider a church like this . . .?' Followed by a description of any church, some of them sounding utterly bizarre.)

I'm coming to recognise those phone calls. If I answer the phone, the caller is noticeably polite; and when Matthew speaks to them, he too has his specially polite voice. And there's that particular blush which tells me, 'This phone call is a preliminary interview so do NOT interrupt or distract.'

That's when I plant a kiss on his nose.

Or maybe friends in other parts of the country will tell Matthew about their vicar leaving, and Matthew will take the initiative to write to those responsible for appointing the successor.

Or—my pet hate—maybe someone on the grapevine will think Matthew would 'do well' (as they say) at a particular church, and he'll be invited to think about it.

'Do well' indeed! What a stupid phrase! I wish there was as much admiration for vicars who 'do well' by hanging on in there in a hard-pressed, poor, vandalised estate that nobody's heard of (never mind cares about), instead of putting all this emphasis on full and successful-looking churches. I know they're important, but they can't be a measurement of a vicar's so-called 'success.' After all, Jesus didn't come to the posh churches. He came to a place which everyone else considered 'not good enough' for them. A stable. *And* it was empty.

Tuesday 21 April

Phone call from a lady, Annie, whom I've met occasionally in church: she comes once or twice a year.

Could she talk? To me? It had to be me. She needed to.

'I'll put the kettle on. Come straight round,' I said. I knew she'd been ill with cancer and wondered if her condition had deteriorated sharply. She had sounded quite urgent. Was she afraid?

'It's not that I feel I'm gonna die yet,' she confided, coming straight to the point. 'But it's at that stage where I've had enough.'

She told me of the discomfort; the embarrassment of having a leaking wound; the terror of going out lest she got caught somewhere with no loo. She felt she was losing all control in life.

'And there's the pain. I don't think I can take much more o' this,' she said.

There were no tears. She was too weary even to weep.

I asked if anyone understood what was going on for her. Her husband? Friends? The doctors?

'People say I'm marvellous, yer know Jane,' she explained, her haunting eyes wide. 'But I'm not. They say they understand, but they don't, yer know. They're ready to be sympathetic, yeah, but you don't want that. Yer just want to be normal again. Don'cha?'

Annie begged me to tell her that she wasn't alone.

34

'You did feel the same as me when you were this ill?' she asked, almost pleadingly.

I assured her I would never forget, I was sure, the awful lonely drudgery of pushing myself through life.

Annie had read my book, *A Pathway through Pain*, and as she spoke of it she reminded me again of the heightened reality of life, as well as death, during those painful years of illness.

'I guess that every atom of your being is screaming at you that you can no longer even push one foot in front of another,' I said with feeling.

'Yeah,' she agreed readily. 'But I couldn't talk to Matthew, yer know,' she went on, not so much apologising as explaining. 'I'm afraid. He might pray with me. I don't want me last rites.'

I wished silently that people could see prayer more as a state of being than a weird preparation for death.

I said, 'You sound as if you need someone very close to share your load.'

'That's it, Jane!' she said. 'I do.'

Some time—but it could not be then—some time, I might be able to tell her without making her feel evangelised, that there is Someone who is indeed very close, who longs to share our load. But we put much energy into keeping Him at arm's length.

That day, I simply listened, feeling useless. Prayed that God Himself would reach out to Annie and let her feel the comfort she so desperately needed.

Wednesday 22 April

Post arrived halfway through the morning while Marmaduke was here for coffee.

Letter addressed to Matthew and myself bearing a large crest. We were intrigued and opened it immediately. In front of Marmaduke.

It turned out to be from the Bishop of another diocese. The post of Diocesan Communications Officer was becoming available, and would we consider doing a job share?

Fortunately we had read in silence. Matthew hastily put the letter down and tried to turn the conversation to 'important things' which Marmaduke had come to discuss.

The moment we were alone again, we read the letter more fully. The post would combine Matthew as a vicar in a small, rural parish; the Bishop thought that we would be a 'strong team' if I also brought my 'communications skills' towards work on behalf of the diocese.

Out came the map to find the name of the village, west of Hull. It was absolutely tiny.

Matthew seemed pretty nonplussed.

'Not what I'd envisaged at all,' he said. 'What do you think?'

I simply shook my head.

At least that one was easy!

Thursday 23 April

Read an article in a Liverpool diocesan magazine about Imperfect Vicars. (For some reason, this was written anonymously.)

It suggested a scheme run on the same principles as a chain letter:

If your vicar is not that good, copy this letter and send it to six other churches who are tired of their vicar. Then parcel up your own and send him to the church at the top of the list.

In one week, you should receive 1,634 vicars. ONE of them should be perfect!

You must have faith in this letter. One church broke the chain and got its old minister back in three months.

Friday 24 April

I'm sure Marmaduke suspects.

It must stem from Wednesday when we'd been unnaturally silent after that letter had arrived about the diocesan communications post. Because there's one thing you can say about Marmaduke, it is that he is disconcertingly quick to put two and two together.

He came round to the vicarage again this afternoon. Sort of ultra-casually; as if he were just dropping by.

'By the way,' he said about halfway through his drink, pretending that this was a mere aside, 'if ever you want a reference, you can rely on me to write one for you any time.'

He grinned: but only in order to give himself time to study Matthew's expression, then mine.

I'm proud to note that neither of us gave away a flicker.

'Matter of fact, I've written one already. I'd just need to run off a copy . . . for whoever doesn't know you well enough to shortlist you.'

He handed Matthew a crisp sheet of A4. There was very little typing on it. I read over Matthew's shoulder.

To Whom It May Concern
Re: REV M GRAYSHON
The Rev Grayshon assures me that he believes in God, and I have no reason to doubt this statement.

You will be very lucky if you can get him to work for you.

Yours sincerely,

Marmaduke

Saturday 25 April

Day off. Brilliant day out in Wales. Three-mile walk over hills near Moel Ffammau; picnic looking down on beautiful panorama of lush green fields.

Returned home refreshed and ready to face the world again!

Sunday 26 April

Arrived at Beersheba at the last minute, to find a circle of people around the church door looking glum.

Joined the circle and peered inside. Several people, including Matthew, were using large brooms to sweep up glass from all over the floor.

Glanced up at the church windows. Seven more had been smashed.

Even when the mess had been cleared and we were

allowed in, our feet crunched the fragments underfoot as we walked into church.

Did NOT kneel down to pray!

Overheard someone complain that the service was late beginning.

Spent the entire service asking God to teach me how to forgive people for whom complaining seems to comprise their whole vocabulary.

Monday 27 April

Day punctuated by Matthew appearing regularly (at feeding times), his clothes more covered with window putty each time.

Tried to cheer him up.

Failed.

Reassured myself he'd have been even worse had I not even tried.

Found myself looking backwards at what might have been. Last time Matthew spent the day replacing windows I had been clinging to the hope of release from a church dragged down by problems of a run-down estate. Now that hope of escape had evaporated.

A pretty grim day.

Tuesday 28 April

Phone call from the Archdeacon. Could we 'pop over' and see him?

'We?' I asked.

'Both of you,' he said.

We made a date. Tomorrow morning.

Wondered if his urgency meant this was important. Archdeacons have a lot to do with the fabric of churches. Maybe he had some scheme up his sleeve to help Matthew over his window repairs?

Matthew predicted that it would be about another job.

Wednesday 29 April

Matthew was right. The Archdeacon began by asking Matthew his thoughts about moving on: was this the right time? For Matthew personally? For the parish?

Matthew reflected on his seven years so far as vicar, and the way that the two churches had grown from raw beginnings as new churches in Runcorn New Town.

'People's faith has deepened tremendously. It's a bit like the birth of a child: they've come through the toddler stage and they're ready to become more independent. It's time for me to go; to leave them to become more independent. They need someone different now.'

The Archdeacon seemed to understand. He turned to me.

'And you, Jane?'

I came straight to the point. 'I just want to have everything settled,' I said. 'The sooner the better.'

'You seem excited at the thought of leaving. Does this mean you're not happy in Runcorn?'

'No, it doesn't mean that,' I replied. 'I'm fed up with yo-yoing around with all this business of shall we/shan't we? We don't seem to be able to shrug off the feeling of restlessness here, so if that means we should move, it's exciting to think of getting to the next stage.'

'I think,' he spoke wisely, 'that feeling unsettled is often a God-given gift: his way of easing us out of the present and steering us to what's ahead. Especially if we are also presented with other possibilities.'

It was his turn, now, to make his own observations on Matthew's ministry. He described how he'd watched things grow and develop, both in the parish and within Matthew himself. Gently, very gently, he came to talk about how Matthew's strengths could be utilised and developed further in a new setting.

He chose his words carefully, telling of one church in the diocese whose vicar had just left. It was in that part of the diocese which Matthew had specifically said he did not want to go; but could Matthew suspend that in order to consider the church? Because so many of Matthew's proven strengths were matched to what that church was looking for.

He passed across a folder containing a profile of the church. We flicked through several pages of explanation: what sort of services they had, when, and how many came; what activities went on both on Sundays and through the week; which groups had special provision, and why; who else worked for the church as well as the vicar.

We saw immediately that this was a church which saw itself as a beacon of hope for the unemployed, those on drugs or alcohol, people being rehabilitated after prison or other trouble. Its ministry was evident in the whole community, and not just for its Christian members. It aimed to offer a place of belonging for those whom the world finds hard to love.

The Archdeacon told Matthew that the Bishop and his staff had all considered that, because Matthew had proved he could work where life was tough, he might be the right man to begin afresh here.

'I place the ball in your court,' he concluded. 'Take the profile: read about the place, visit it, pray about it. Come back to me within the week. Now!' And he rubbed his hands together. 'Let's see what's in the fridge for lunch!'

We drove home virtually in silence. Both of us had been hit by the unexpectedness of a proposal such as this. It caused us to re-examine our motives for moving on.

If escape had featured anywhere on my agenda, it was definitely not to be found in this proposed parish.

I was left with a question. How prepared was I to move to a parish which may be yet more dispiriting than Runcorn on a bad day?

Thursday 30 April

Unable to sleep. Churning things over and over, round and round in my mind. Kept repeating to myself—or was it to God—that, if God wants us to go to a hard parish, then I most definitely wanted to say yes. We'd go.

Yes, but. Every time I said yes, I added a but.

. . . But hadn't we been through a hard enough time with all the vandalism and accompanying pressures at Beersheba?

. . . But we were weary of vandalism. Couldn't we have a turn at a 'nice' place now?

. . . But what about all Matthew's other gifts? He'd had no chance to exercise half his gifts where we were—no one place is a sufficient forum, and particularly in an embryonic church Matthew had not had the scope to work to the breadths he was capable of.

. . . But what about the children? Schools? Family life?

Longed to say 'Yes' to God without a 'But.' Disappointed in myself that I didn't seem able to make it. My faith seemed so impoverished.

Then found an anger within; an anger which rose the more I dwelled upon it. Fancy Matthew being asked to go to that parish! It was ridiculous! Had they considered how much Matthew might need a change, instead of more of the same? They could only have been trying to fill a gap on their map. Or so it seemed.

Was the implication that it's wrong for a vicar to want to spread his wings a bit?

. . . But then, if we wouldn't go, who would?

Was pleased to learn that Matthew, too, had found it hard to sleep. And even more pleased to find a unity between us, for he, too, felt heavy-hearted and even angry at being asked to go to that church.

'I can't even face going to see the place,' he said wearily over coffee. 'I remember it all too vividly from meetings I've been to there.'

I agreed.

'It's a God-forsaken place,' I said. 'Except, a church cannot be that.'

'Which is exactly the rub,' mused Matthew. 'If we say we don't fancy going there, what are we actually saying? That we'll only go where *we* fancy? That can hardly be "Obedience"!'

I sighed at the weight of the challenge. Only yesterday morning I had read Jesus' first words to His disciples. Simply, 'Follow me.' Were Matthew and I saying we were *un*willing to follow?

Or worse: if we found a different parish—one that we fancied—would we quote those very words back to God? Would *we* be the ones to say, 'Follow me' to him? Only, we'd couch it in words like, 'Please bless us,' or 'Please let Matthew get this job'—but in fact all we'd be doing would be clamouring to take over God's rightful place as leader.

No conclusions.

May

May

Friday 1 May

Phone call from Pete.

'Happy May Day!' he greeted me.

'Thanks.' My voice was pretty flat.

'I'm ringing to cheer you up,' he said. 'D'you want to hear about our babysitter being bewildered by Zachary's version of the Lord's Prayer, or would you prefer to stay glum?'

'Try me,' I said.

'She couldn't work out what Zachary meant when he'd begun praying very seriously, with his eyes tight shut, "Our Farmer with chickens."'

'But Pete, what did Zachary mean?'

'Well, he'd got so quick at saying, "Our Father in heaven," that it had got slightly abbreviated to "Our Father in hen." So when he'd forgotten "hen" he'd used the nearest word he could remember: "Our Father with chickens". Good, eh?'

Saturday 2 May

Matthew phoned two of his best buddies from college days. They were friends in whom he could confide; safely distant enough for Matthew to ask them their reaction to the Archdeacon's suggestion.

The second one put everything in a nutshell. 'Look mate,' he said amicably. 'A man can work with a pick-axe for so long, but after a while he needs to swop for a different instrument. Otherwise his blisters will burst and turn nasty.'

He gave Matthew the courage to trust his own instinct—and mine—that he was looking for different challenges in his next appointment, not more of the same.

Matthew finished composing his letter to the Archdeacon at half past midnight.

As he flopped into bed, I commented that if he'd been on a bigger salary we could at least have inspired ourselves with a sumptuous meal out tomorrow.

Sunday 3 May

Woke abruptly to find myself in the sort of situation which is a mere nightmare for most people. This was for real.

Matthew burst into the bedroom, panting from having leapt up the stairs two at a time, flinging off his dressing gown as he came.

'Promised I'd do an 8.15 communion for another vicar,' he panted. 'It's at Dick Fence's church!' (Dick's church was five miles away.)

The digital clock beside the bed had just changed to 8.12. I realised that Matthew had been in his study for the past hour or so, having his usual pray and bit of peace and quiet alone before the 10.30 morning service. He was neither washed nor dressed, never mind shaved.

My heart lurched.

'Don't worry,' I tried rather lamely to reassure us both. 'You can use your 10.30 sermon for them.'

Matthew grunted some agreement, pulling his cassock straight on over not much else.

Trying desperately to do at least something to help, I dragged myself out of bed, outside into the rain with only my nightshirt on, to get the car out of the garage for him.

Matthew bounded out to the car after me.

'Thanks,' he panted as I opened the door.

8.14. And it was at this moment that I realised that I was about to be landed in it. Because if anyone was going to telephone to see why Matthew was late, it wasn't Matthew who would give his apologies. I would have to do it for him.

Already my mind was whizzing with possible excuses—all half-truths, I was ashamed to discover. Like, 'Sorry, the car wouldn't start.' (Well, it hadn't, first try). Or, 'He must have got held up in traffic.' (He'd surely have had to slow down for someone, somewhere, on his way?)

I leaned through Matthew's window.

'PLEASE tell me what I should say if they ring?' I begged.

'Just tell them the truth,' he said simply, shooting backwards down the drive.

How do vicars make it sound so easy to be good?

Did Matthew realise how awkward I felt, covering for his faults? Did he know the responsibility it seemed to me, keeping people sweet? And anyway, whereas they'd have spoken specially politely to the vicar, they might not have been quite so reverent towards his wife. The fact was, I was likely to be the recipient of all their ire.

I trailed reluctantly back into the house and eyed the telephone, daring it to ring. Had an incredibly strong urge to lift it off the hook so nobody could get me.

Thought, Does anyone know how much a vicar's wife can feel terrorised by the telephone?

Wednesday 6 May

Zachary phoned. Zachary! And he's not yet three.

'Hello Aunty Jane.' He sounded as if he were making an announcement.

I said hello.

'I saw—I saw—a man today on his bike.'

'Did you Zachary?' I enthused, wondering what had made this sight memorable.

Jo, in the background, straddled the conversation, speaking half to me and half to Zachary.

'The man was showing off a bit, wasn't he, riding without using his hands,' she explained.

'Yes,' Zachary agreed. 'And—' (big breath), 'And —' (another breath), '—Aunty Jane?'

'Yes, Zachary?'

'He wasn't handling his bars.'

Friday 8 May

8.30 am   Another early morning phone call just as I was setting off to take the children to school.

Answered with rather an early morning growl.

Immediately heard the pips of a call box.

'Is that the vic'ridge?' It was a girl's voice. I had little doubt that this would be a baptism enquiry.

'Yes.' I was somewhat curt, I'm afraid.

'I'm ringing about Beersheba,' she faltered, her voice shaking. 'It's full o' smoke. I can't gerr in—it's chokin'. The minister's norr in. Should I phone the fire brigade?'

My heart was suddenly pounding.

'Dial 999 and tell them all you can,' I instructed. 'And I'll tell the vicar. I'm sure he'll come straight away.'

Yelled up to Matthew, taking his shower after breakfast. He dressed and was out within minutes.

51

Children found this rather exciting.

10 am Matthew came home looking pale and drawn.

'The b******s!' he said from the car as I went out to greet him.

I assumed he was quoting the firemen's words, of course.

'What happened?' I asked straight away.

'They attacked the place with blow-lamps in the night,' he began. 'Melted the windows. Couldn't break them, so they melted them instead. Took a blow-lamp to them. The b******s!'

He stepped out of the car. I was immediately hit by the over-powering stench of smoke clinging to his clothes and hair.

'And?'

Matthew stopped to lean on the open car door. 'They must've stopped when the curtain went up in flames, which in turn set the ceiling smouldering. Meanwhile, all the molten plastic which had slid to the floor was so hot, the wooden floor caught. Floor and ceiling have been burning very slowly for a couple of hours, according to the firemen's assessment. It's a miracle the whole place wasn't burned to the ground!'

I could hardly take it all in.

'Apparently it takes a good 20 minutes of holding the blow-lamp directly on one piece of window for this to happen. They're just bent on destruction.'

'What's happening now?' I asked.

'The firemen are still there, and so's Luke.' Luke was the minister who shared with Matthew in every aspect of ministry at the two churches. 'He's devastated too, poor man. I've come to change before I touch another thing. It's all filthy. Filthy! Like a sticky tar clinging to every surface: every book, every bit of organ, everything. The place will be unusable for months. I need old clothes now.'

6 pm   Matthew returned, his pallor showing beneath his grimy black face.

'Can't face tomorrow,' he said.

We'd booked to go to a conference in Derbyshire, about how Christians can have renewed zeal in their local churches. It seemed a pretty forlorn hope as far as Beersheba was concerned.

We tried to sell our tickets, but unsuccessfully.

Decided that if we wake up in time, we'd go. It just might be worth it.

Saturday 9 May

Went, after all, to renewal conference.

First song: *'Let the flame burn brighter . . .'*

I was not amused.

Reading: the Bible story about Nehemiah. The reader began, 'The wall of Jerusalem is broken down, and its gates have been burned with fire.'

Entire morning talk was based on these verses. I could not believe my ears! It was as if the programme had been planned specifically for us by someone who knew every recent detail of our situation.

At lunchtime, we heard a whoop of pleasure from an old friend, Gerald. Excited greetings were quickly replaced by deep sympathy and understanding as he listened to Matthew's story of the past 24 hours.

'I believe God has had his hand on you and the conference organisers, for today to be so apt,' he remarked, full of faith. 'He must want to speak to you.'

He called over one of his friends from their church group. The three men joined together to pray and listen to God. I slipped off to give the children some lunch, quietly thanking God for people prepared to share Matthew's cumbersome burden.

By the end of the day when we said farewell to

Gerald, both Matthew's and my spirits had been lifted. Matthew had not only the strength to face tomorrow, but also renewed enthusiasm.

With evidence like that, it would have been difficult not to believe in miracles.

Sunday 10 May

It happened to be Matthew's turn to take the morning service at Beersheba, while Luke was at the second church, St Mark's.

As people arrived their faces fell at the sight of the smoke damage. Matthew stood in the doorway directing them to the church hall opposite. Then he processed into the hall for the start of the service and looked at them.

'I've just realised why you all look so bewildered this morning,' he said with a slightly mischievous tone. 'You ladies, you've been coming to Beersheba for years and years, and you all know one another by where you sit! We'd better all introduce ourselves to one another, seeing as you've all been ousted from your own pews in the church!'

There followed a very moving service. Everyone sang with gusto songs like, *'God's not dead!'* and *'We shall overcome.'*

Afterwards I spoke to Luke's wife, Rachel.

'D'you like going to bed with a kipper, then, Jane?' she giggled as we commiserated with each other about our husbands stinking of smoke.

Rachel's bubbling faithful optimism inspired me.

Lunchtime was interrupted by a phone call.

Not for the first time, I had an urge to throw that contraption out of the window.

It was Gerald.

He told Matthew that he and the carload from his church, north of Southampton, had talked of Matthew for much of their journey home. At their service this morning they'd prayed for him together. Gerald himself had had a picture of a tree with new shoots growing steadily, but clouds had been obstructing the sun's light. Gerald observed that, if this was an image of the church in Runcorn, they should be praying for God to allow his light to lift the cloud and dispel the darkness.

Matthew was enormously encouraged by the call. He had a distinct spring to his step as he returned to the lunch table.

'Ooh, and by the way,' he said, stuffing too much potato into his mouth as he finished reporting his conversation. 'Gerald said that he wanted to keep supporting me by praying for me, so he wants to keep in touch. He invited us both to go down one Sunday evening when I've no service here. We've fixed up a date next month.'

It was brilliant to see Matthew so buoyed up.

Monday 11 May

We both woke very early.

Matthew broke the quietness. 'That picture Gerald had . . .'

'Yes?'

'It's true, isn't it? You know, the tender new shoots—that's a very accurate description of the new Christians here. And Gerald's strategy for praying for the light to dispel the darkness: he's right, you know.'

He turned to study my face carefully.

'I think this might mean we should stay in Runcorn.'

It felt like a strange relief.

'For how long?' I enquired. 'Years?'

'Until something comes to me. I'm going to stop looking. Completely.'

'Great,' I replied, relaxing into his arms. 'Let's go for it, man!'

Saturday 16 May

Invited to a luncheon party to celebrate a couple's 40th wedding anniversary. Knew hardly anyone else, but met some fascinating people.

Several knew of me through reading my books.

'I read your *Confessions of a Vicar's Wife*,' said one. 'Only I laughed so much, I hurt my back!'

I sympathised but expressed my disbelief, especially as she was laughing as she spoke.

'It's true,' she answered me. 'I hurt it so much, I had to buy your book on pain next!'

Matthew, pursuing her ability to see the funny side, said, 'I say! The publisher would be quite interested in your story: I mean, there is a certain potential for future advertising strategies . . .'

After the delicious food came the champagne and speeches. It was the first time Matthew and I had heard the background to this couple who, in church, are quietly self-effacing, but whose lives abroad had been pioneering and, as we learned, enormously fruitful.

'And behind every man,' said the husband, extending his arm towards his wife, 'is a wonderful woman.'

We all clapped and cheered.

Matthew piped up, 'Ah, but do you know the other side of that old proverb?'

There was an expectant hush.

Matthew quoted a card he had once received.

'Behind every man,' he said with a twinkle, 'is an astonished mother-in-law!'

Sunday 17 May

Greeted by Albert the moment I walked into church.

'I don't know how we're going to cope with the fame, you know Jane,' he said with a wink. 'We've been put on the map now, all because of your book.'

He looked very pleased and important.

He went on, 'I mean, nowadays what I'm asked is not, "Do you go to Matthew Grayshon's church?" No. The question is, "D'you go to that church with the Vicar's Wife?"'

Tuesday 19 May

A researcher from ITV wants to talk with me about my writing. Made a date to visit on Thursday.

I told Matthew at lunchtime.

'Oh yes?' he said, decidedly unimpressed.

I wished I'd chosen to tell him in a different mood. He could be quite adept at cutting people down to size. Too late, I sensed he might try now.

He said, 'Bill and Ben this time, is it?'

I tried not to be amused. That would only encourage him.

He winked.

'Are you going to be the weed?'

Thursday 21 May

ITV researcher came.

She picked up my *Confessions* and chuckled at the front cover.

'Oh, but this is WONderful!' she said.

She turned it over to the photograph on the back cover. No twinset and pearls but—shock horror—a vicar's wife wearing lipstick, and a vaguely risqué dress.

'MARvellous!' she repeated. She'd thought that a writer about suffering could only ever be serious.

She proceeded to tell me about her curate's wife. ('Hers'? I thought. Do parishioners really believe that they possess the curate and his wife?)

Told me of her sense of fun, her independence from the traditional role of a clergy wife.

I asked whereabouts this was.

'Oh!' she replied. 'They're the curate in Fulham.'

I froze.

'They're the curate?' I asked.

She stopped for a moment to listen to what she'd just said.

'*They*?!' I repeated with a glare.

She saw her mistake.

I buried my head in my hands. 'Is it simply not possible for any clergy wife—even one whose hall-mark is her independence—to be free from the web of her husband's job?' I asked.

What I did not show this ITV researcher was that, while vicars' wives can display horror at the presumptions people make, I knew there was also a distinct privilege. It could only be a compliment to this curate's wife that her input was so valued to be counted worthy of mention.

Saturday 23 May

Spontaneous visit from Dick Fence who arrived clutching a bottle of wine.

'Have you heard about the parish east of Liverpool?' he asked as he poured generous portions into our glasses in the kitchen.

Matthew and I looked at Dick blankly.

'Their vicar's just announced he's leaving,' he explained. 'I thought you'd know. They obviously know you.'

Matthew raised one eyebrow.

'They've named you as a possible successor. Said they want you. Even told the Archdeacon.'

'That's nice,' said Matthew. 'But I won't apply.' He took a swig.

It was Dick's turn to be surprised.

'I'm not looking for a new job,' Matthew explained.

'Cheers!' Dick raised his glass. 'Are you set on staying here, then?'

Matthew nodded.

'I'll drink to that!' Dick gave a huge wink.

Before he left at the end of the evening, Dick turned to Matthew once more. 'Just let's get this straight. You won't even apply for that job?'

Matthew shook his head. 'I won't apply to any church, anywhere, unless I'm specifically invited, by them, directly. That's my litmus. If that doesn't happen, I'm staying here.'

Dick went away very happy.

Thursday 28 May

Marmaduke must be under-working again.

Called round on his way home from work today announcing that he'd had enough of all the pieces of paper that get dished out in church. A notice-sheet every week, words for songs (copyright obtained), agendas for future meetings, minutes of past meetings . . .

'I believe this all goes to show, Matthew,' he said, 'that we worship the photocopier.'

'Oh yes?' Matthew could see the twinkle in Marmaduke's eye.

'Yes.' Marmaduke was successfully maintaining a straight face. 'We might as well have a FESTIVAL OF PHOTOCOPYING. I've drawn up a proposed Order of Service.

His listed hymns included:

'Type the good type',
'A4 all the saints',
'Angels from the reams of glory'.

Saturday 30 May

Letter from Chrystal, a friend whose husband used to be at theological college at the same time as Matthew.

Brief summary of her news, but her reason for writing was to tell us about a vacancy coming up soon for a vicar north of Southampton. We must have heard of the church. She and her husband Duncan had both commented on how suitable Matthew would be there: he had the confidence to follow in the footsteps of a well-known, well-loved man without being threatened himself.

Could they urge Matthew to consider applying?

We read the letter and smiled. It was a compliment

that Chrystal and Duncan seemed to think Matthew worthy of this church. But of course, Matthew and I both knew that the litmus test was negative. Matthew had not been approached directly. Chrystal was a third party.

What seemed absolutely extraordinary was that this was the same church, north of Southampton, which has recently become so supportive of Matthew. It's the church which Gerald attends.

Our visit, arranged last month, is in just one week's time.

June

June

Monday 1 June

Phone call from Charlotte, whose husband Jonathan went to college with Matthew and is now a vicar.

She'd just been browsing through this weekend's papers. Had we seen the situation vacant at the church north of Southampton?

I said no, that Matthew wasn't looking for a job.

She sounded slightly crestfallen.

'Oh,' she said. 'That's a pity. Because we thought the description was exactly Matthew!' Her voice regained its former enthusiasm. She went blithely on, 'We used to go there before we were married. We've just been saying how suitable we think Matthew would be there. He'd follow after the previous chap marvellously. We had to tell you. It's exactly the church where we could imagine Matthew.'

I thanked her but remained very non-committal.

'D'you think he'll apply?' she urged.

I wished she'd been speaking to Matthew. I was uncomfortable at discussing such an important issue on his behalf.

I replied that I didn't know, that I believed it was a matter between Matthew and God, and that I should not interfere.

'Goodness!' she snorted. 'How d'you do *that*?'

Replied that I wasn't sure. Merely observed that it is possible to react with great enthusiasm to what looks like God's will, and to rejoice very loudly. So loudly, in fact, that we do not hear the quiet whisper of God's still, small voice.

I had made that mistake once and was determined not to do so again.

The moment Matthew returned home I reported Charlotte's telephone call.

Matthew listened, smiled, then rooted through the pile of church papers to find last Friday's. Turned straight to the advert and read it out.

The church sounded brilliant!

Wondered what on earth Matthew would do. I know he's made his sort of covenant with God but this is very close to being approached directly.

Wished God made things clearer sometimes. I feel as if I'm in a fog.

Evening Today's Bible reading was about Moses meeting with God on the mountain, when God gave the Ten Commandments.

Noticed that the mountain had been shrouded in cloud.

Was very encouraged. I'd always imagined that meeting God closely, or hearing him speak, would necessarily involve total clarity of vision. Never thought that it could happen while we're shrouded in cloud!

Asked God to meet me in this present cloud of unknowing.

Tuesday 2 June

Phone call from Gerald.

'Hi!' he began. 'I'm in America.'

My mind immediately raced. He'd never phoned from America before: this must have been urgent. Was something wrong?

'I can't stop thinking about Matthew,' he told me. 'I've been praying for him again this morning. And it seems to that, if he sees the sort of job he's looking for, he should go for it.'

I noted down what he was saying without asking any questions. Quite apart from the fact that every second of conversation was costing Gerald money, I felt that the purpose of the call was not to chat but to convey a message.

'I know he has a pact with God and that must be honoured. But will you encourage him from me, not to be so firm that the Holy Spirit can't move him?!'

I giggled but Gerald remained quite serious. 'I really feel that if something shouts as being the very sort of place he's looking for, then he must have his eyes open to an open door. Anyway, see you on Sunday!'

Told Matthew as soon as he returned from his visiting.

He held the note and read it until he must have known the words off by heart.

I held my breath to hear what he would say; what he would do.

He brewed a strong coffee for us both.

As he took the first sip he asked, 'Well, d'you think I should write off for the application forms before Sunday's visit, or after?'

Sunday 7 June

At least this Sunday we didn't have to keep silent about visiting another church. Somehow it seemed more wholesome that parishioners knew where we were off to, and they pledged to pray for us this evening as if endorsing and joining in with the prayers of Gerald.

The only aspect which they didn't know was that the vicar of Gerald's church was leaving, and Matthew was therefore Looking, too (capital L!).

Had a wonderful welcome from Gerald, still jet-lagged, and his wife. No mention at all of the fact that Matthew had requested details and application form for the post as vicar. No, Gerald's interest and support was for Matthew the person, wherever his job was.

Drove to the church for evening service. My heart quickened as we entered. Felt on 'red alert' to hear God's voice say either, 'Not here!' or, 'This is the place I've planned for you.'

Full church—about 400 or 500 in the congregation. Singing was terrific: a very fulsome sound. Atmosphere animated and expectant. There was a special service with opportunity for individuals to come forward for prayer—this was why Matthew had specifically chosen to come tonight. There was space for about 12 at a time to have hands laid upon them as prayers were offered by the ministering team, of whom Gerald was one.

Matthew went forward and joined the queue. A space became vacant at the rail and he knelt down. It happened to be the turn of Gerald to lay his hands on Matthew's head and pray. But others followed—more than usual, I thought. They stood in a circle around him. One fixed her eyes above Matthew's head: she looked so inspired, I wondered what she was seeing.

Suddenly, as I stood at Matthew's side and held his hand, I was aware of a surge of deep peace. This was like a moment of anointing. Matthew and I were in exactly the right place. We were meant to be

here, I was sure of it, supported by these praying people.

I was equally certain that this was a picture of what was to come. And that the lady with her eyes fixed above Matthew's head had seen the same.

On the way out of church, at the end of the service, a man opened the door for me.

'Goodnight, Jane,' he said with a warm smile in his eyes.

I stopped, astonished at being addressed by name, by this man I had never seen before.

He grasped my hand.

'Don't worry, you don't know me,' he said. 'But we know you, and we're right behind you in everything. We'll keep praying!'

Was sure that this was yet another sign, another promise for our future.

When we flopped into bed, Matthew said, 'Extraordinary!'

'What?'

'I've had a picture in my mind of the church building where I'll be next,' he said. 'That church east of Penzance was the right shape, but the light was all wrong. The moment we walked into Gerald's church tonight, I recognised it. The shape, the sense of space, the airiness, the way the light filtered in—everything matched the picture in my mind. Extraordinary!'

Everything was pointing in the one direction. Before I slept, I prayed that I would trust God to steer this ship, not me. Told God I wanted to listen to Him. Begged Him not to lead us up the garden path!

Friday 12 June

Matthew posted off his completed application form.

It felt like a very important day.

Saturday 13 June

Took Zachary to his first every concert at the Royal Liverpool Philharmonic Hall. It was a concert geared specially for young children: African music played by Africans in full costume, and a team of dancers who flung themselves energetically around the stage to the beat of the drums. Both our children were enthralled.

Zachary was thrilled from the moment he reached the auditorium. He eyed his seat carefully as I lowered it for him to sit down. He plonked his bottom at the back of it and his little legs didn't even reach the edge of the seat.

'It's prickly!' he said, rubbing the material. He was only wearing shorts.

As I let go, the sprung seat swung upwards, bringing his legs with it. I pressed the seat down for him, let go and exactly the same thing happened again.

Thought, Oh dear! He's too light; maybe he's too young after all?

Matthew leaned along and suggested I should take Zachary on my knee.

'No thank you!' came a chirpy little voice.

Zachary's legs popped up again. He pressed them down again. He began to laugh. Then again, up, down. Up, down. His eyes widened in delight.

'I like this concert!' he cried gleefully.

His pleasure brought back my own delight as a child. Decided not to tell him off (as I had been) but enjoy the adventure at his level.

I said to him, 'I remember when I was little, *I* used to do that with my seat.'

Zachary stopped swinging and stared at me disapprovingly. I wondered what was wrong. What had I said?

Zachary began to glower, as if I could not understand him at all.

At last, he sighed. 'When I was little, I didn't come to concerts,' he said. Then he placed each arm on the rest at either side of him, as if he were an executive city gentleman. Chairman of the Board. Clearly, he was very big.

At the end of the concert Zachary ran to Pete and Jo, waiting outside.

'Did you enjoy the big drums and the lovely music?' they asked.

'We sat in swinging seats!' was all he would say.

71

Thursday 18 June

Matthew's been shortlisted!

Not really a surprise. More accurately, a confirmation of what seems to be right.

Interviews in ten days. Wives expected to go too.

I didn't think that was a very personal invitation but was prepared to forgive them.

Friday 26 June

Collected Jo's skirt to borrow again for Monday's interview. Ironed all Matthew's and my clothes. Polished shoes.

Had to laugh at ourselves. Both of us were standing side by side with one foot up on the wall outside, polishing away, getting the best shine, wanting to be seen at our best.

Supposed it got rid of nervous energy.

Saturday 27 June

Beautiful afternoon. I escaped the house for a walk alone in the sunshine. Was able to think my own thoughts and prayers, instead of being bombarded with the children's constant chatter.

Back home, knelt in my favourite prayer corner. Allowed my thoughts to dwell on the picture which a friend, Sandy, had embroidered as a present for me:

Wait for the Lord and He will help you (Proverbs 20:22).

Thanked God because we had waited, and He was helping now.

Sunday 28 June

Very excited. During the notices in church I sat thinking, Well! This time in one week, one of the notices Matthew may well be making will be the announcement of his resignation! After eighteen months of waiting, this definitely feels the right time. God's time. God's place awaiting us.

Exhilarated by the sense of being enfolded by God's loving purpose, and being led to pastures new.

Monday 29 June

Took train to interview. I couldn't sit still; wanted to chat all the way. Matthew didn't. He wanted to read all the way.

Not a harmonious journey. I was glad Matthew wasn't wearing his dog-collar.

Half way there I noticed the title of Matthew's book: *The Irrelevant Church.* Thought the interviewing panel's confidence in him might be rather shaken if they saw it.

Prayed that none of them would see it.

Read over the schedule for the two days of interviews:

Monday
An 'Informal lunch'
Meet four different leaders within the church (3/4 hour each)
Tour the parish while undergoing discussions with a church worker
Tour the town while discussing the parish with a different church worker
An 'Informal Evening Meal'
Stay overnight with our hosts—ours were psychologists

Tuesday
Interview with the Bishop
Interview with the full staff team who work together (7 clergy)
Interview with two church wardens

I took God's hand and asked for strength!

Arrived at a little hall at the back of the church, to meet the church representatives who would conduct the interviews. Of the four others being interviewed, Matthew and I knew two from theological college. Said enthusiastic hellos, hugging one another in a rather unAnglican manner. Were called to order by a church warden.

While he welcomed us I studied the other short-listed candidates carefully. Caught myself judging them by their appearance. Felt guilty. Worse, realised that much of my judgement was based on what the wives looked like. Felt more guilty: if anyone else had done the same with Matthew I'd have declared them to be totally unfair!

Surreptitiously adopted a more ladylike and becoming posture.

We were led upstairs to a larger hall where about two dozen people, members of this church's congregation, awaited us. Their stance was reminiscent of a vulture whose prey had just come into sight. They appeared to feel awkward, however, called as they were not only to participate in choosing their next vicar but also to show Christian love and compassion towards the poor candidates.

The warden clapped his hands and asked for silence. Pointed to the tables set out for six people and issued instructions. Each interviewee was to sit, opposite his wife, on the middle chair at a table. They'd be joined by four parish members—one on either side—to talk during the soup course. At that point, the candidates were to remain seated while all the parishioners would move to a different table. More conversation, with four different people, during the main course. All change again for the dessert, and finally for the coffee.

He said the same process would be in operation at this evening's informal meal. That way, each candidate would meet 32 parish members.

Good GRIEF! I thought. They call this 'informal'?!!

He smiled.

I coughed, spluttered and almost choked.

His speech continued, urging us not to consider this an interview *per se*, although we should know that anyone who had any comments or opinions about candidates had been invited to report them to him by midnight, so that the interviewing panel would have feedback on parishioners' impressions in time for tomorrow morning's formal interviews.

He said grace and everyone scrambled for a table.

I whispered to Matthew, 'What d'you reckon they'll give us? Spaghetti bolognese, to test how much we spill down our chins? Minus marks for anyone who sucks a long piece?'

He grinned in reply. 'Followed by those cream cakes which spurt out jammy cream on the first bite you take.'

It was a bit like musical chairs, except the candidates, remaining seated, felt as if they might be accidentally sat upon at any moment.

I survived it all. At one point I was asked, 'Will you support your husband in everything he does?' The woman questioning me looked so over-serious, I answered her with a grin, 'Not if he runs off with another woman, no! I won't!'

Fortunately, she became a little more lighthearted.

In Round Three a physiotherapist landed next to me. I warmed to her immediately. She said she was into massage. Added that she found that people really begin to talk with her while they're being massaged.

'Ooh!' I said. 'Maybe Matthew should try doing massage on his parishioners?'

All six of us at the table began to contribute to the idea.

'If you think about it,' we continued, 'some people get terribly up tight when talking to a vicar. They might find massage very beneficial.'

Our laughter increased as we built up the joke, so much so that people from the other end of the hall turned round with little less than glares. They seemed to infer that these candidates were vicars, after all, and should not laugh too much. This was a very serious and solemn occasion.

Found myself thinking, Hang on. Could I survive in a parish where laughter is frowned upon?

Spent a fascinating afternoon. Engaged in some penetrating conversations. Felt privileged to be in on this process.

While being shown round the church buildings, the warden pointed out the tea-making facilities. I noticed him looking at me. I admired the tea urn but refused to show any hint of personal interest. Did NOT want to land myself with a job as vicar's wife *cum* tea-maker. Made sure the warden showed Matthew the kitchen as well.

We heard about the successes of the church, the fruits, the growth in numbers. Nobody seemed to talk about the unsuccessful areas of the church's life. Jesus had spoken of how blessed are those who hunger: it sounded as if, at this church, people were filled with good things. Was this right?

Perhaps the impression we both had was not representative of the whole church. How could we know?

Remembered the title of Matthew's book on the train. This church would definitely not like to consider itself irrelevant. What would anyone who lacked faith think?

Evening   Exhausted. By the time we met our hosts I was ready only to kick my shoes off and curl up in a heap on the sofa.

I didn't have a grain of energy left to contemplate the fact that they were both psychoanalysts.

Tuesday 30 June

6 am   Woke early, refreshed and with a clearer mind. Alone before God, I pondered some of yesterday's questions. Was particularly aware of the niggling discomfort after hearing so much about the church's enormously successful and wide-ranging ministry.

Matthew was not chasing success. He had been through so much of a private, unnoticed pain—the pain of watching pain—he could never disregard suffering. For 15 years he had seen me dragged in and out of hospital, from one operation to another, never knowing with each episode whether he might in fact lose his wife. Matthew knew all too well that God is not just a God of miracles, but he is also Lord of suffering. He's a God whose Holy Spirit leads His people into the desert: and not just 'bad', or 'unfaithful' Christians who have 'lapsed', but all of us. Even Jesus, perfect as He was, was led into the desert, not as punishment nor as a sign that He was 'burnt out' or exhausted in His ministry. He didn't even begin to preach or do miracles before He had experienced the desert. The desert was the starting place of Jesus' ministry.

Matthew was looking for a church which was ready to face up to the reality of suffering. He would want to be a pilgrim together with other Christians on a journey which at times passes through dry and barren and dispiriting land. He would want to bring God's refreshment, of course, but he would also want others to refresh him too. He would not be happy in a church which pretended that faith is an oasis which goes on for ever!

Would he, then, be happy at this church?

Our perception yesterday was that Matthew would have been introducing a foreign language if he had begun to talk like this. Many of those whom we met could have felt restrained, distracted from their elation at God's visible miracles.

Concluded that, if Matthew is to take up the reins of such a challenge, he would need every ounce of conviction that it really was God who had led him here. Because it may be that some parishioners may not want the discomfort he would undoubtedly bring.

Lunchtime Matthew went into the formal interviews like a lamb to the slaughter. He had an hour with the wardens, an hour with the Bishop, and an hour with the other clergy.

I sat in the little ante-room watching the faces of the four candidates as they came out of each grilling. Tried to read, but of course I was much more interested in listening to their comments. Had quite good fun comparing what each one had been asked.

On the train coming home, we both said how much we'd enjoyed the two days. It had been unusually stimulating.

We had to admit, however, that we were both left with hesitations. Matthew was absolutely in two minds: should he accept or decline? We'd been so sure it was God who had led Matthew to apply; the 'call' had been quite unexpected. Should he, therefore, accept, despite this one fairly major hesitation?

Matthew said the worst thing for him would be if he were offered the job.

Evening The phone call came as soon as we arrived home. Decision made for us. They didn't think they were the right church for Matthew; nor he for them.

Both felt oddly relieved, yet also devastated. It seemed a denial of all that had felt so right for the past month.

Had we been wrong to believe that this had been God's will?

What about all those 'coincidences'? From the time of the fire and the conference, everything had been working together towards this—or so we'd thought. Gerald's picture; Duncan and Chrystal's letter;

Jonathan and Charlotte's telephone call; Sandy's verse; the church building exactly matching Matthew's vision; our own excited feeling that this was right . . . was that all wasted?

Pete and Jo arrived with a bottle of wine. Found me pretty tearful; Matthew was more contained.

We decided to indulge in an Indian take-away meal. The two men piled into the car to collect it while Jo settled Zachary in bed upstairs. I sat numbly looking across to my little praying corner. Saw once again Sandy's embroidered verse.

Wait for the Lord and He will help you.

Had a distinct urge to smash the frame. We'd waited so long! All month we'd trusted God to help us: all, it seemed, for nothing.

Jo took ages to come downstairs. I could her singing softly. I was impatient to be comforted in the same way that she was comforting Zachary.

For the first time, I focused on the first word of Sandy's verse. It told me quite clearly that we had to wait.

For how on earth long?

Intense gloom.

July

July

Wednesday 1 July

Gloomy.

Thursday 2 July

More gloomy.

Friday 3 July

Staff lunch all together. Matthew was appalled at himself that he should be so totally exhausted. His colleagues thought it was very healthy—even if tiring—to face one's true reaction instead of hiding from it.

Saturday 4 July

Exhausted. Mentally and physically exhausted. Couldn't muster the energy to do a thing.

Seemed a waste of a day off.

Sunday 5 July

Sat in church as if in cloud of gloom. Especially during the notices when Matthew was not, after all, announcing his resignation.

Instead of today being the beginning of a new adventure for us, it was as if I had to endure all the usual everything. Everything was as always. The routine seemed to have become a rut.

Wanted to kick everyone up the backside. Couldn't we get out of this rut? The rut of people coming up to me with their complaints that 'Matthew had said he would do this and he hasn't,' or, 'What shall we do about the summer fair?'

Wanted to reply, 'I'm sorry, I can't decide for you. And I can't face this sort of complaining!'

Knew these thoughts were most horrible, uncharitable, ungracious, unholy. It wasn't as if there was much complaining at this church, anyway. It was just that even a little was more than I could tolerate.

Tried to console myself that I am not the only person in this world who can have thoughts which are horrible, uncharitable, ungracious and unholy. Knew, however, that such consolation was empty.

Evening   Returned to the church later to pray alone. Found myself weeping. Saw how very ugly I am on the inside, with all my horrid verbal quips lurking there, unseen by all except God and (occasionally) myself.

Felt strangely comforted. Knew I could not depend on my own strength, on my own apparent 'niceness', to be acceptable in life. Felt totally at the mercy of Jesus.

The surprising comfort was that I sensed this to be the most blessed place to be.

Monday 6 July

A new week. It began with Stella, our neighbour from across the road, ringing the bell. At 8.30 am.

'I'm sorry it's so early, Jane,' she apologised with her bubbling laughter. 'But it's me car. It won't start. Could Matthew possibly give me a jump start?'

Matthew willingly found his jump leads and set to work. Stella and I stood in the drive, arms folded, chatting. Told one another that this was how to give a man moral support.

'Actually, Jane, I must tell you this,' Stella said. 'The girls in my office give me very funny looks when I tell them stories about living opposite your vicarage.'

I was surprised. 'What d'you mean?' I asked. 'What stories?'

'The first time I went into work late and announced that I'd had a jump start from the vicar . . . ooh, Jane, you should have seen their faces!'

Tuesday 7 July

Reminded myself of the old formula when I was working in research: a negative answer is very positive. It means progress.

Wished we could see more progress in finding a new parish!

Wished God would speak. You know, Talk! Say, 'Move,' or 'Stay in Runcorn.' Either would be fine. I just want to know.

Recalled how one chap was apparently 'guided'. He'd heard God speak to him directly, he said.

It happened when he was at Bible College. He was a very devout man: very prayerful. Trouble was, he was also loud in his prayers, so he really got up everyone's nose. Night after night he used to pray, loudly, 'Lord, show me where to go. Guide me. Speak to me, Lord!'

Bit like Matthew and me now.

He went on like that for an hour in his bedroom every night. No one else could sleep.

I suppose he was asking for it. His fellow students in the adjoining rooms got together and decided they couldn't bear it any longer. So one night, one of them stole into his room before 'Mr Devout' came in, and he hid inside his wardrobe. It was terribly squashed and cramped, apparently: he had to curl up in the most dreadful position.

Anyway, in came Mr Devout. Sure enough, he knelt by his bed and began to pray, 'Lord, where am I to go? Please guide me. Speak to me, Lord!'

Right on cue there came a deep, booming voice which spoke very slowly from—as it were—nowhere.

'Go—to—Africa!'

At that moment all the students eavesdropping at the door expected a moment of realisation as to what had happened; they expected him to open his wardrobe and let out the student behind the voice. They thought this would be the end of the long, loud prayers.

They couldn't have been more wrong.

Mr Devout raised his voice and began praising God, thanking him for speaking so clearly. He got quite caught up in rapture, so much so that they didn't feel they could interrupt! And the poor chap in the wardrobe was too embarrassed to climb out. Despite the most terrible cramp, he stayed in hiding. Altogether it was an extremely awkward situation.

I believe that Mr Devout is in Africa right now.

The story goes that, no matter what his fellow students tried to tell him, he said he was convinced that it was God who had spoken to him quite clearly one night and told him to go.

Maybe God speaks through even our sinful ways.

Wednesday 8 July

Sudden idea. Could I fit into our bedroom wardrobe?

I could practise my most booming voice and say— well, whatever place *I* fancy . . .

'Go—to the—Bahamas!'

That could sound quite good.

Wonder what Matthew would think?

Sunday 10 July

Special service to re-open Beersheba after the fire two months ago.

Frances, one of the musicians, slipped round to the vicarage before the service with a proposed list of songs:

It only takes a spark to get a fire going
Melt my heart O God
So light up the fire, and let the flame burn
Spirit of the Living God . . . melt me

Monday 11 July

A warm sunny day, with a balmy wind blowing from the south. As soon as the children had left for school I treated myself to a quiet walk along the sandy beach near Hilbre Island.

As I walked, I turned my thoughts God-wards. It felt a brave step. I knew that, for ten days or so now, I'd been keeping God at arm's length. I'd been covering up my real emotions ever since Matthew was rejected by the parish north of Southampton—for that was how it felt—a rejection, whether or not Matthew in turn would have accepted their offer.

The truth was that, despite all my courageous-looking efforts to keep my chin up externally, deep inside I had been hurt and disappointed. I felt as if God had picked us up and filled us with hope, and then He'd let us down. And I had avoided telling Him face to face (as it were), because it felt too impertinent to talk to God like that. Instead I had hidden: immersed myself in other activities, trying to survive on ridiculous little arrow prayers. I had not dared to give God any decent quality time, specifically listening to Him.

Underneath my bravery, I was afraid.

I was surprised at the sense of relief as soon as I had acknowledged what I'd been doing, to myself and to God. It was as if I no longer needed to hide from my own failure. I was strangely comforted by the acceptance I felt God to be offering, refreshing me within just like that warm Sahara breeze in my face.

I walked on, enjoying the sensation of water splashing my ankles and calves.

The picture of Sandy's verse came to mind once again:

Wait for the Lord and He will help you.

So many times I had looked at that verse and smiled to myself, a self-satisfied smile. Right up until the day of Matthew's interviews, I had read it as if it had said, *You can stop waiting for the Lord now, because He has already helped you.*

Slowly, very slowly as I splashed my way through

murky pools beside the sea, it dawned on me that I had got my tenses all wrong.

Before God could guide me at all I had to be prepared to wait, and keep waiting.

I turned my face towards the sun as I prayed that God would create in me a new heart; one which was more prepared to submit to Him no matter what happened.

Wednesday 15 July

Pete phoned. 'Happy start to the school holidays!' he said gleefully.

I thanked him and asked if that was his only reason for phoning.

He said, 'To celebrate I took Zachary to the zoo this morning. When we saw the giraffe house there was a giraffe looking round the wall. Zachary said, "Oh look, Daddy, there's a giraffe with a roundcorner neck!"'

Thursday 16 July

Letter to Matthew from a Bishop in one area of London. He's known Matthew quite well for some years.

This morning's letter says there's a church in west London which he thinks is just right for Matthew.

I thought despairingly to myself: And how many times have we been through THIS before!

But all I said was, 'Blooming cheek! *He* can't decide what's right for you, dawlin'!'

Matthew read on. There was a paragraph describing the church. It sounded ultra-traditional.

'Hardly inspiring!' I said. I didn't want to know about a boring old church. Good grief—Matthew might turn into a boring old vicar then, and who wants THAT? Or, worse, would that make me a boring old vicar's wife?

Heard Matthew say he'd ask the Bishop for more details.

I refuse to take ANY interest in this AT ALL.

Monday 20 July

Another letter from the Bishop, replying by return to Matthew's request for more details. It happens that he's coming to a conference where Matthew will also be, this coming week. He suggested meeting Matthew there.

I said, 'I do hope you won't give the Bishop the impression you want to go to that boring old place in London.'

Matthew was very quiet.

Monday 27 July

Matthew set off for his conference. A three-day affair. As I waved him off I thought, Right, I can spend the whole three days writing, at least during the children's school hours. He's made contingency plans for every possible problem so—in theory—the parish can stand on its feet without him.

Decided not to act as his secretary but, instead, to leave the answerphone on.

Sat down to work at 9.15 am.

At 9.30 the doorbell rang. Deliberated over whether or not to answer it. Thought it was extremely anti-social not to.

Didn't recognise the lady. Her car was a Volvo so I knew she was unlikely to be from our parish.

She was refreshingly polite and friendly. 'I'm dropping these letters off for Rev Anderson. I gather he's coming here at 11.00, bringing two clergy visitors from India whom he's showing around.'

Oh NO! This suggested an hour or more of my

time, to welcome them and chat to them. All I wanted was peace to concentrate: was that impossible in a vicarage? I'd switched off the phone but now the invasion was coming through the door.

My open-mouthed silence must have shown my dismay.

'Rev Anderson told me last night that he thought this would be a good idea,' she smiled.

I said, as calmly as I could, 'Actually, Rev Anderson hasn't checked that anyone will be here at 11.00. Matthew's away. And I . . .'

At that point I had to think very rapidly. It would have been untrue to say I would be out, and I couldn't tell a downright lie. If I said I was 'busy writing', she might not know how much one interruption—however brief—can stop the flow. She'd think I was being awkward; belligerently unhelpful.

'. . . and I will be at work by then.'

'In that case,' she smiled, 'I'll deliver these directly. No problem.'

I decided she was a nice lady.

'But what about the Indian visitors?' I asked bleakly. Would I be disobeying the command to 'practise hospitality' if I didn't give up my work to welcome the visitors? 'If the only welcome they receive from us is a closed front door, that's hardly Christian!'

The nice lady answered for me.

'It shouldn't be your job to mop up everyone else's mistakes,' she said. 'Rev Anderson ought to have checked first. He'll have to find a solution for himself.'

Her smile broadened. 'You are allowed to live your own life, including going to work,' she said.

I agreed wholeheartedly. In theory.

I wished it were easier in practice.

11.30 am Rev Anderson didn't appear. I guessed that the nice lady must have got a message to him.

My concentration had still been dinted. Not a good day's work.

Tuesday 28 July

Still hoping for a day of writing without interruption. Decided to go for it. Switched on answerphone and told myself to ignore the door.

Sat down to work and thought, But they'll see the car parked in the drive! They'll know I've returned after driving the children to school.

Got up and put car away in the garage.

Sat back down to work and thought, Oh dear. Last time someone called and got no reply at the front door, they walked round the back to see if we were in the garden. If they do that today they'll pass my study window and see me at my desk. *Then* what'll they think?

First idea was that I could dive under my desk to hide. Imagined the picture. Thought, how ridiculous!

Second, better idea was to lock the side gate.

Got up to do so. Took quickest route, climbing through my study window. Thought, If anyone could

see me now, and the lengths I go to to keep the privacy of spending one day without interruption, they would think I was crazy!

Unless, of course, they thought about it.

Wednesday 29 July

Matthew phoned. Said he'd met with the Bishop.

'What did he say?' I asked.

'Can't say,' he said in an unnaturally guarded voice.

I asked him what on earth he meant, tantalising me like that.

He whispered into the phone, 'I'm surrounded by clergy with their ears flapping.'

I asked him questions to which he could answer yes or no, thus imparting some of his information to me without giving any juicy gossip to them.

'Did you get on well?'

'Yes.'

'Did he tell you more about this church he thinks will be so wonderful?' I did not conceal the sarcasm in my voice.

'Yes.'

'And?'

'Yes.'

'Well—did it sound as deadly as we first thought?'

'No.'

'Did you trust him?'

'Yes.'

'I mean, are you sure he's thinking of what's best for *you*? Or is he only thinking of what will be best for whatever the church is that he has in mind?'

'An interesting question.'

'Not just interesting, dawlin'! Important!'

'Yes.'

Most frustrating.

Thursday 30 July

Matthew came home from the conference glowing.

'I spent about an hour with the Bishop,' he reported. 'That parish in London sounds good, my lady.' He was so pleasant I found it hard to fight him.

'Oh yes?'

'The people are ready to grow. They can see that God's at work, and they want to understand more of what it's all about.'

I raised my eyebrows, listening to him.

'Well, that's exciting!' he enthused.

I couldn't disagree, but would not be drawn into any emotions about it.

Matthew told me more details. Said he'd apply. Ugh, what a drudgery, all over again! Shortlisting, interviews: I could do it in my sleep. And all that mental energy for a church I don't even fancy!

Fixed my thoughts on tomorrow. Our summer holiday begins.

Friday 31 July

Set out immediately after school for three weeks of holiday. Hurrah!

Told Matthew that I intended to hibernate from absolutely everything to do with ANY parish, past, present or future, for the ENTIRE duration of our time away. ALL conversation about work is banned for three weeks from NOW.

August

August

Friday 7 August

Matthew has slept for almost the entire week. Still, this is normal for the first week of holiday. The pattern is usually:

Week One: He sleeps.

Week Two: He's grumpy.

Week Three: He's back to being the amorous man I married.

Saturday 8 August

Had a row.

This heralds the onset of Week Two of our holiday. It's almost as predictable as pre-menstrual tension.

Wednesday 12 August

Matthew being very extra-specially wonderful and nice. Two days early: progress is good.

Friday 21 August

Today I'm 37 and a half.

Why do Christians aged 37 and a half write diaries?

Anyway, mine is not so sacred.

Evening Began journey home. Realised that we'd be travelling round the M25 and would be passing very near the parish which the Bishop thinks is so perfect for Matthew.

Matthew suggested we could drop in on our friends Emma and Charles, a couple of miles beyond the North Circular Road, from where he could drive round to the church.

I felt exceedingly reluctant to agree. However, knew it would be jolly unsporting to say so. Knew it would be a shame to spoil our post-holiday good moods.

Steeled myself for the ordeal.

Emma and Charles were in. Gave us a lovely welcome and urged us to stay for lunch. Matthew phoned a Church Army officer working for the nearby parish, who quickly agreed to show him round.

I stayed looking after the children. Waited for Matthew to get back saying, 'No, the place was awful. You were right to be hesitant, dear.'

He didn't. He came in saying he could get quite fired up about it.

My heart sank but I smiled with an enthusiasm which impressed me.

Emma and Charles pressed us to stay overnight so we could talk further into the evening. 'And then you could go together to look at this parish, Jane.'

I deigned to drive with Matthew, after the children were in bed, to see this church for myself.

Arrived to see it was lovely. Beautiful! We walked around it in silence. A peaceful silence. The birds were singing their evening tunes, and rabbits nearby scampered over the common. It wasn't like a London bustly church we'd envisaged at all: more like a village church, at the end of a long cul-de-sac. It even had a majestic yew tree outside.

I kept hearing the phrase, A church isn't a building, it's people. And we still had no idea what the people here were like.

For the first time, though, I allowed the faintest chink into my armour.

For the first time I conceded that perhaps I should not reject the idea that this *might* be God's place for us.

Friday 28 August

The day for the adverts in the church papers.

Matthew said he was *not* looking at any other jobs on offer.

I looked instead. Found an interesting looking church in Brussels.

'This is more like what we want,' I said. 'Listen. *'Dynamic priest sought'*—that's you. *'French an advantage for family life'*—hey, that'd be great! My favourite subject at school, and my headmistress always said I should have studied French at university instead of doing nursing. The children would grow up bi-lingual. *'Open to fresh possibilities'*—oh YES!' I was positively trembling with excitement.

Matthew was distinctly interested. I could tell by the way he was trying so hard to keep his face expressionless.

But he repeated firmly, 'I am not looking.'

This is intensely frustrating!

Saturday 29 August

A friend from Bristol came to stay with us for the Bank Holiday weekend. She asked about the jobs scene.

I told her about Brussels. 'Sounds GREAT!' she said enthusiastically. 'MMMmm.'

Matthew told her about London. 'Oh,' she said, her voice decidedly flat. 'Oh.'

I thought that spoke volumes.

Sunday 30 August

Spent as much as possible of the day either speaking French, or speaking English with a strongly French accent.

By evening, Matthew commented, 'I think I should remind you that, if we want to go to a French-speaking place, the Chaplaincy at Bordeaux would be infinitely more suitable than Brussels.'

'Oh?' I said, pleased that my subtle hints had at least got through to him. 'Why?'

'Matter of principle,' he said. 'The wine's better in Bordeaux.'

September

September

Tuesday 1 September

New month. Autumn tints beginning. The end of an old season; beginning of a new.

I've resolved today that I shall not begin again where I left off before our summer holiday, with so much thought to moving—or not moving. I shan't get sucked into even thinking about that. I shall live as if we're not moving.

Wednesday 2 September

Both children complained that their school uniforms were too small. I was tempted to reply that they could just hang on for a little while, because Dad may get another job, in which case they could jolly well squeeze themselves into last year's uniforms until we moved. However, I then remembered yesterday's resolve.

Bought new uniforms ready for the new term. This is the 'We are settled in Runcorn' approach to life. If Matthew says anything about appointments or interviews, I shall allow it all to wash over me. Let everything happen around me.

Thursday 3 September

Noticed there's an evening class in Assertiveness beginning soon at the College of Further Education. Came home and told a few friends that I fancy signing up.

'Heaven help us,' muttered Marmaduke. 'You don't need more!'

Then he turned to Matthew. 'I think there should be a course for spouses of any Assertiveness pupils.'

Matthew smiled smugly. 'I've found the very thing,' he said.

Marmaduke was interested. 'Karate is it?' he asked.

Matthew looked very pleased with himself. 'It's called Navigational Skills.'

Friday 4 September

Spoke to my publisher, Henry. He drew comparisons between myself and another author who is, he said, 'very diffident'.

I said, 'Excuse me, but what do you think I am then?'

He chuckled. Sounded hesitant; on the edge of embarrassment.

'You're very non-diffident, Jane.' Sounded pleased with himself, as if he'd just been tactful.

I wondered what he meant by that.

Evening At Radio Merseyside to record a new series about The Vicar's Wife. Just getting into the swing of my first paragraph when the producer interrupted down my headphones, 'Um, your voice is fading a bit Jane . . .' He was adjusting his dials while he spoke. 'Not sure why . . .'

I explained, 'It's because I get shy. I'm very shy you know. I need to learn how to be assertive.'

He fell off his chair, hysterical with mocking laughter and shocked with disbelief.

Sunday 6 September

In church sang, *Let me have my way among you*.

I thought: Never mind assertiveness. God asks for our submission. And there aren't many adult learning courses about that.

Monday 7 September

Jo phoned. Told me she and Pete had decided to celebrate the end of Pete's school holidays by having a cooked breakfast. She had bacon sizzling under the grill before Zachary had plodded downstairs, having been dressed by Pete.

'Morning!' he'd said, quite the young man. He looked at the cooker, then up at Jo.

'Are you cooking tea?'

Jo had explained that no, this wasn't tea, it was breakfast; that they'd decided to have bacon and egg for breakfast as a special treat before Daddy had to start going out to work early again.

Zachary had gazed at her disbelievingly.

A few moments later, Jo had asked Zachary to get knives and forks out of the kitchen drawer.

'For tea?' he'd asked.

Once again Jo had replied no, this was not tea, this was breakfast. A different sort of breakfast.

Another suspicious look.

Finally, the three of them had sat round the table for their bacon and eggs. Pete had asked Zachary to say grace, because he loved to cover his eyes and peep through his open fingers in order to thank God for it. Normally he itemised every piece of food on his plate ('Thank you God for my nice meat, and my yellow 'tato wif a bit on it, and my 'mato, and my 'mato seeds in the middle, and my bwead wif cwust on . . .').

Today he'd covered his eyes tightly and prayed simply, 'Thank you God for my nice tea.'

Jo had whispered, 'Breakfast, actually!'

Zachary began again, 'Thank you God for my nice bweakfast.' Pause. '. . . TEA!'

Tuesday 8 September

Thought about Zachary and his grace. Realised what a parable it is: I ask God about something (which parish next?) and I do not hear His answer, any more than Zachary heard his Mum and Dad's explanation. We can be on a different wavelength; it seems sometimes as if God is answering different questions from what we've asked. We can't understand until we've grown up more.

Thanked God for Zachary, and asked for patience until I've become mature enough to understand God a bit better.

Wednesday 9 September

Philippa returned from her third day at school beaming.

'We had painting today, and I did a big picture all over the wall,' she said.

She took off her coat. Her new grey skirt was absolutely covered in paint. Non-washable acrylic paint.

I exploded. 'You didn't wear your apron!' I shouted. 'We can't possibly afford to buy you *another* skirt!'

Philippa shuddered and crept upstairs. She kept her distance until I had calmed down. Poor girl, she couldn't have known the weight of anxiety which lay behind any mention of new school uniforms.

Friday 11 September

Phone call from the Bishop in London, to say Matthew's been shortlisted.

I might have guessed he would be.

I determined to stick unswervingly to my decision not to get emotionally involved in any prospect of moving.

Matthew replaced the receiver and perched on a stool in the kitchen. Told me the interviews will be for 6th October.

Both of us felt pretty blank. I commented that at least we'd be more objective in weighing up the job if we weren't blinded by excitement.

Sunday 13 September

At church in the evening, Luke, leading the informal service, asked us to share a little about what we considered to be a very significant aspect of our lives at the moment, in order that we could pray for one another appropriately.

I thought, But I can't say anthing! I'm on the brink of a life-changing event and I can't tell them!

Felt very left out.

Monday 14 September

Philippa's eighth tooth fell out.

Tuesday 15 September

Philippa expressed great delight that the tooth fairy had left 20p under her pillow.

Wednesday 16 September

Tea included sweetcorn.

Philippa's face lit up. 'Hey!' she exclaimed. 'Each piece of sweetcorn looks like a tooth!'

We supposed she was right, but wondered why this made her so excited.

'Well, if I took one piece of sweetcorn—a pale coloured one—the tooth fairy might think it really was a tooth! I could put a tiny stone inside, so it's the right weight, and I could paint a tiny red dot for the blood, and they would never know. Then I'd get extra money.'

Her eyes were alive at the prospect. She couldn't understand my hesitation.

'If I did it lots of times,' she assured me, 'the money would help to pay for my new school uniform.'

I decided, most definitely, that when we went to the interviews in a fortnight, we would not be taking the children.

Friday 18 September

One of Philippa's schoolteachers came running up to me as I kissed the children goodbye. She looked very concerned. Asked if she could have a 'quiet word' with me at the end of the afternoon.

Spent all day thinking, Oh no. This is IT. Philippa must have been recommending her ideas for setting up a fraudulent business with tooth fairies, and this teacher disapproves.

Smartened myself up before returning for the

appointment in the afternoon. Felt more prepared for battle.

Arrived at school full of ideas on How To Apologise.

Turned out that the teacher wanted to talk about a matter which was nothing to do with my children. She wanted a reference from Matthew. Did I think he'd mind terribly? She didn't like to ask him herself. Would I ask for her? She'd be so very grateful. She even offered a bottle of wine as a thank you to him.

I told her I was sure Matthew would do it, and managed also to give her the name of my own favourite wine.

She then told me how dreadful it was applying for jobs and not knowing where she'd end up. Said I had no idea.

I decided I could bear it no longer. Told her Matthew was thinking about a move, too. Explained that it wouldn't just be the job that was different, but also we'd inevitably have to move house, probably move to a different part of the country. New job, new area, new friends; everything.

Immediately felt guilty for breaking the secrecy bit. Gave the excuse that of course I'd needed to ask her advice about the children changing schools.

She was very nice. 'I really feel for you actually,' she sympathised. I thought she was referring to the uncertainties, but she went on, 'Because people will be watching you. I remember when our new vicar came, we watched his every move with intrigue. How he dressed, how he spoke, everything he did, poor man.'

She giggled.

Not sure whether her sympathy was countered by the sense of foreboding.

Monday 21 September

Zachary's third birthday. Jo baked him a dinosaur cake, because his current insatiable craze is for dinosaurs.

A dozen little friends went to his party. Unfortunately, when Jo walked into the room with his cake for him to blow all the candles out, she had not noticed that Zachary's mouth had been full of sandwich. She did not know to make sure he had swallowed before he threw all his enthusiasm into blowing out those lovely candles. Thus he took a deep breath and, as vigorously as he could, blew them all out.

The dinosaur cake was splatted with half-chewed peanut butter sandwich.

The children thought the cake was scrummy!

Granny, watching the whole scene, declined a piece. Told Zachary that she was sure it was delicious, really, but she had teeth which could find dinosaur cake hard to chew.

Later, Pete was tucking Zachary into bed when the little voice asked, 'Daddy, what happened to your Granny?'

Pete replied, 'She died, I'm afraid, which made me a bit sad.'

'When did your Granny die?'

'It was a long time ago, Zachary.'

Pause.

'Was your Granny like the dinosaurs?'

Saturday 26 September

Out for a day's walk on the Welsh hills. It was a very cold, autumnal day. Decided to call in at Pete and Jo's on our way home. We arrived just as they had lit their coal fire for the first time this season.

'Quick, Uncle Maffew, come in!' Zachary called excitedly as he opened the front door. He raced into the lounge ahead of us, pointing to the flames in the hearth.

'All the candles are having a party!'

Granny was there for tea, too, and we all sat round chatting. Zachary decided to join us by the fire. He drew his small plastic chair into the circle as if it were a huge armchair and made himself comfortable. He placed his hands on his knees, precisely, adopting a most adult pose. I watched him study Granny's face carefully. He was concentrating.

There was a lull in the conversation.

Everyone turned to look at Zachary, who leaned forward nearer Granny's face.

Very seriously, he said, 'Granny, you haven't got teeth like me, have you?'

Sunday 27 September

Sermon series at St Mark's beginning this evening with the first one on Pacifism. Luke was to preach, Matthew to lead the service.

Frances came round with a list of songs which the music group could play. Would Matthew like to show this list to Luke when he arrived at church? It read:

Fight the good fight
Onward Christian soldiers
Soldiers of Christ arise
In heavenly armour
The battle belongs to the Lord
The heat of battle rises
The strife is o'er, the battle won.

October

October

Friday 2 October

Phone call from Nellie, one of the church wardens at the church in London, offering for us to stay overnight at her home on Monday night, and would we like her to meet us off the train?

I thanked her. 'How will we recognise one another at the station?' I asked.

'Oh, I'm sure I'd recognise a vicar and his wife any day,' she said.

I raised myself in my chair. 'Steady,' I warned.

She laughed, an infectious giggle which gave me permission to continue.

'What would you do if I said I have a purple punk hairstyle?'

Without hesitation she replied, 'I'd say my three teenagers would be delighted!'

We laughed together and chatted. I felt at ease. Nellie exuded a bubbling kind of warmth.

At the end of the call, I put the phone down feeling slightly happier about Tuesday's interviews. Though, on the whole, I'm still dreading having to go. It intrudes upon the resolve I made on 1 September.

Evening Reported this afternoon's conversation to Matthew, who told me I'd been very slow. I *should* have agreed with Nellie that we'd recognise one another straight away because Matthew would always know a church warden when he saw one.

Saturday 3 October

Saw Pete and Jo. I asked Jo if I could borrow her skirt again.

'What, another interview?' she grinned. 'Isn't it about time you bought your own interview skirt?'

'Next time I will, I promise,' I assured her. 'If there is a next time.'

Monday 5 October

On the train to Euston I looked at Matthew and myself and said, 'You know, considering how much thought we put into what we'd wear for your interviews back in April, we're a bit laid back this time.'

Matthew said, with feeling, 'We're just being ourselves.'

Evening Stayed overnight with Nellie and her husband. Got on like a house on fire, talking mainly about hill-walking. Matthew observed that London is far too far from the Lake District, never mind Scotland.

We touched briefly on the subject of tomorrow and Matthew asked Nellie how she would describe the church.

'We're hungry spiritually,' Nellie answered. 'And thirsty.'

Hadn't our whole experience at the church north of Southampton shown us that Matthew was looking for a church which was exactly that: hungry and thirsty?

I hadn't realised until now what an important lesson we had learned there. I had thought that that time had only been painful. Only now did I glimpse any value from it.

Nellie seemed anxious not to speak only for herself, but to represent the viewpoint of a diversity of people within the church.

'We're a big mixture of people,' she said. 'And we're just ourselves. We need someone who can accept us as that—and then lead us on.'

From Matthew's squeeze of my hand, I sensed that this church was getting many metaphorical ticks in Matthew's book. He has used those very words about ourselves on the train travelling south.

Tuesday 6 October

Chatted with Nellie over breakfast before leaving for the church. Teased her rather a lot that she looked so smart for the interviews. She had replaced last night's jogging suit for a smart blouse and skirt, and her trainers for a pair of court shoes. I suggested she should have been equally smart last evening if she'd wanted to impress.

Quick as a flash, Nellie pointed to Matthew fixing his dog collar to his shirt, and pointed out that they were two of a kind.

We arrived at the top of some steps at the back of the church and stood for a moment watching everyone milling around with cups of coffee. I felt slightly conspicuous as the only woman. Out of four candidates, no other wives had come.

We were herded into a minibus to tour the parish. Viewed the houses and community facilities, stopping occasionally to get out and inspect places. The Rectory was absolutely beautiful with a quiet sun-drenched garden.

By the time we reached the daughter church, it was full of ladies for their Lunch Club. Someone explained to the Chairwoman, 'Excuse us. We're just creeping in discreetly to look at the place . . . we're showing round all the candidates whom we're interviewing . . . (knowing nod; voice dropping to a whisper) . . . the new Rector you know.'

Any ideas of our 'creeping in discreetly' were flattened immediately. Every single lady at the Lunch Club turned, goggle-eyed as we filed past. I thought it would have been fun to break into the cancan for them; however, everyone else was being very seemly.

Returned to the main church. A beautiful building. The embodiment of a traditional church. This was the kind of church which gets filmed.

Inside there were three galleries all round. Huge pulpit, but I noted that half the congregation could hide behind the pillars and the Rector would never see what they were doing.

I thought, Must remember to warn Matthew about that, if he gets the job.

Walked down the aisle and was nearly at the front when I noticed a label strategically placed on one pew.

It said, *Rectory Pew.*

Thought to myself, There's one place I'll never sit in this new church, and that's in this pew!

Nudged Matthew with a snigger.

'I didn't like to tell you about that,' he whispered. 'I saw it when I came round with the Church Army captain in August. Told him you'd not only make sure it was removed, but that you—personally— would take the screwdriver to it yourself.'

'How did he react?' I asked, intrigued.

'Mixture of total disbelief and schoolboyish delight! He couldn't imagine what the congregation would say!'

We were being moved onwards. Lunch was in the adjoining hall. The Bishop and several other clergy arrived. Formal interviews began immediately after-

wards. At that point, I went back to Nellie's house for a rest. Matthew faced the questions alone. *He* is the clergyman, not I. I am his wife, not his co-worker.

I lay down, grateful for the quietness alone to reflect on the day so far. Pictured Nellie's bubbling enthusiasm; the Bishop's warm smile; Matthew's confident stature; comments made to Matthew almost as if he had been the only candidate. It was odd, but from the moment we had arrived at the top of the steps into the church, it was as if there had been an arrow over Matthew's head, pointing at him as the man for the job. All morning while we'd been jostling around in that minibus, and throughout our lunchtime conversations, that invisible arrow had followed him.

I found only one conclusion. It looked inevitable that Matthew was going to come here. That was the word: inevitable.

I felt suddenly trapped. I wanted to escape. Flee! I followed my first instinct and took the liberty of phoning Emma, our friend whom we'd called to see on our way home from holiday back in August.

'Emma?' I said. 'It's Jane.'

She responded very quickly. 'My dear!' she exclaimed. 'We prayed for you this morning. How's it going?'

I came straight to the point.

'I think Matthew's going to come here,' I said, discovering tears running down my cheeks. I had no idea why. Emma asked me questions, trying to hear what was wrong. My mind was a blur. I could identify no particular reason.

Perhaps I was exhausted by the emotional roller-coaster of the past eighteen months while Matthew had been looking for a new job. Perhaps I sensed that this was the end of that phase, and I could let go and weep. Or perhaps, these were tears over what might have been—the church east of Penzance where I would have been so happy; or north of Southampton where Matthew would have been so excited; or east of Liverpool where we'd have been so much wanted; or east of Hull which would have been so very different.

I sniffed, 'I think I might be finding it hard to trust God that this place is best. It's not what *we*'d have chosen, you know.'

The way Emma listened was very soothing. I didn't really take in what she said, but the effect was to help me to look to God. Ours, she said, is a God who doesn't make mistakes.

'Jane, do you believe that God is in control?' she asked.

What a question!

'Of course I do; it's just that—'

I stopped. What *was* my fear?

Was it simply that I was not used to the passive role in which I found myself now? I have the ability to organise things and I had not organised this. I had not often stood so far back, nor restrained my involvement in a decision which would affect my own life for a matter of years to come. I was not prepared to abandon myself to anyone less than God.

Or was it that I had been taken by surprise? I had scarcely allowed myself to think about Matthew's move since the parish north of Southampton had not worked out. I had been protecting myself, no doubt, after the devastation we had both felt then. I had not wanted to re-open past disappointments, never mind make myself vulnerable to new ones.

And this was all so different from what we had expected. The church itself was different—it was more traditional for a start—and the way in which Matthew had been asked to consider it had crept up on us from behind. With the church north of Southampton, the signs of God's guiding presence had been evident (or so we had believed) but the outcome had been 'no'. By contrast, this time it seemed the outcome was going to be positive, yet we had had *no* visible sign of God's presence. It called for total trust that those in authority making the decisions, were agents of God.

And then I remembered. Back in July when I'd walked along the beach near Hilbre Island, I had decided to trust God *no matter what*. I had prayed—many times—that God would steer this ship, and now that He was I needed to put my whole trust in Him. I was not going to resist Him, just because He was taking us on a different course from the one which we might have envisaged.

I had joked about assertiveness and submission—was I so self-assertive that I could not submit to God, I asked myself?

All I needed to do was to assert God's sovereignty over everything, knowing that Matthew and I had put this situation into His hands, repeatedly.

'It's just nothing,' I replied at last to Emma, chucking at my hesitation. 'I *do* believe that God is in control.'

Matthew returned within an hour to Nellie's house. He'd enjoyed the interviews. We had to leave to catch our train home before they decided which candidate they'd invite.

Arrived back in Runcorn. 'Quick!' said Matthew. 'We'll just get to the end of the meeting at Gerty's house and no one will suspect I've been interviewing for another job today!'

Everyone was choosing Christmas presents out of a mail-order catalogue, in a money-raising effort for the church. Such choices seemed very mundane in comparison with the other life-changing choices of the day. I supposed that, often, the mundane accompanies the extraordinary. Sometimes it consumes it.

Wednesday 7 October

8 am   Phone call. The Bishop.

The decision had been unanimous: everyone on the panel yesterday had wanted Matthew to be the new Rector.

Matthew was remarkably detached. He did not accept with enthusiasm. He told the Bishop he had 'no reason to say no.'

It was strange that neither he nor I felt excited. Just a quiet sense that this must be right.

Must plan when to tell whom, and how. Wonder how on earth they'll react?

Thursday 8 October

Phone call from Nellie. She was absolutely delighted that Matthew had accepted the appointment. Her enthusiasm more than made up for any which we lacked. Had we known that the decision was unanimous? Bishop, Archdeacon, Area Dean, church representatives, all of them were sure that Matthew was the one.

It was as if that invisible hand pointing to Matthew had guided everyone to the same conclusion.

Nellie talked bits of business with Matthew. How to word the announcement. Dates for Matthew to start. They agreed on next March, in time for Easter.

Then Matthew passed the phone over to me.

'I went straight out yesterday and bought all your books,' Nellie said. 'Including your *Confessions*!'

Sudden fear gripped me.

'Don't let anyone read it!' I said urgently.

Nellie hooted with laughter. 'What do you mean?'

I didn't know whether to laugh or panic. 'Reading a book of *Confessions* is hardly as impressive as looking at the CV of your new Rector.'

Nellie continued to think this was very funny. We chatted for ages.

Came off the phone very excited. Behaved as if I was rather manic. Flew up the stairs two at a time and, instead of just bathing Philippa as usual, I dived in beside her.

'What's happened?' asked Philippa.

'What are you so happy about?' asked Angus.

I gestured to close a zip over my mouth.

'We'll tell you tomorrow,' I promised. We had to wait before telling them, because Sunday is the day of the formal announcement which must be in both churches simultaneously, in Runcorn and London. We didn't want to ask the children to keep secrets from their school friends.

'All I can say now is, we've got something *very* important to tell you.' I began to sing.

'What?' they chorused.

'Good news,' I said.

'Please tell us now,' they begged. 'We want to be as excited as you!'

I shook my head. 'Tomorrow,' I repeated. 'Straight after school.' And I leaped out of the bath, singing very loudly.

The children gazed at me in astonishment. Angus was eyeing me with a little suspicion.

I was fairly surprised at myself, actually, as I watched such a surge of unchecked excitement push its way to the surface. Had I been suppressing all my feelings about this parish in London ever since Matthew first mentioned it, by way of defending myself from another disappointment?

It has taken a day and a half since Matthew accepted the appointment for it to sink in that this is definite. Only now can I give vent to my real feelings.

Friday 9 October

Matthew and I sat the children straight down to tell them the news, the moment they came home from school.

'Do you want to take a guess?' Matthew began.

Angus blushed. 'Are we going to have another baby?' he asked. 'That's the only time I've seen you as excited as this, when we were expecting Philippa.'

So that was why he had eyed me with such suspicion last evening!

I quickly said no, we were NOT having another baby, and explained that we were moving house to London. Matthew described the new church.

Both children joined in with the general family euphoria.

Saturday 10 October

Did lots of tummy-flattening exercises.

Sunday 11 October

Matthew announced at both Beersheba and at St Mark's that he had been invited to become Rector of a church in London, and that he had accepted.

The news was greeted with a stunned silence. Hardly anyone moved.

Matthew filled the awkwardness by chatting a little about the new parish. Explained that it was much, much more traditional than these churches in Runcorn: that it had bells rung every week, it had a choir who wore robes, that it even had a special place where the Rector's wife was supposed to sit, which was marked, *Rectory Pew*.

That brought a chuckle to the congregation. They turned to catch my eye. They were amused at the idea of me sitting where I was told, or indeed, doing anything I was told.

After the service, unusually, only a few people spoke to me. Fred came up and said, 'You know, they could put an extra three letters into that pew label and make it read, *CORrectory Pew*.'

Then Tom said, 'Well, if you're moving to London you'll have to learn to sniff mid—' (he sniffed, bringing his arm across his nose)'—sentence!'

Finally, a couple, fairly new members of the congregation, came up to me. The wife was in tears.

'We'll miss you terribly,' she said. Her husband nodded limply.

Their quietness spoke more loudly than words. I was very touched.

Monday 12 October

On her way home from school Philippa asked, 'Why do some people say Rector instead of Vicar, Mummy?'

'It doesn't really matter,' I explained. 'Although some people think Rector sounds more important.'

Philippa tossed her head. 'I don't,' she announced.

Tuesday 13 October

Our longest-serving babysitter, Mildred, dropped in for elevenses. She wanted to ask lots of questions about Matthew's new job, which he answered as fully as he could.

'But why are you leaving, Matthew? You've done so much for us! Things are just beginning—how can you leave now?'

Matthew told her that it was for another man to reap what he had sown. The fact that the harvest was beginning was a sign, to him, that it was truly time to go.

Mildred drank it all in, hardly saying a word. When Matthew had finished she turned to me. 'And how do you feel about it, Jane?' she asked.

I began, 'We—'

But Mildred put out her hand to stop me. 'No, I mean you. As Jane.' Her eyes narrowed. 'How do *you* feel about it all?'

I found myself stuck for words. Nobody had asked me that question. Nobody. They'd asked about the church, about the area, the schools, and I'd given them the facts. But no feelings.

I chose to answer very honestly. 'I'm not sure yet,' I said. 'I've only met one person so far. She was very nice. Oh, and the other wardens I saw very briefly. But I've no idea what the church is really like until I've been to a service. So all I can say so far is, I know it's right. I've had moments of being thoroughly excited but otherwise I've nothing to go by.'

Mildred nodded.

Matthew was staring at me while sipping his coffee.

He looked ever so serious. Concern rose in me: did he disapprove of my being so open in what I said?

'Is that OK for me to say that, Matthew?' I enquired.

He looked up with a jerk. His face was furrowed. He muttered something or other which I didn't catch, but I sensed disapproval, and so did Mildred. She left pretty hastily.

All through lunch I braced myself ready for Matthew to tell me I had shared too closely with a parishioner. By the time we'd finished I couldn't bear the strain any longer.

I said, 'Are you disappointed with me, man?'

He looked baffled.

'By what I said to Mildred? When I told her how I felt, you glowered.'

'Oh, that? I wasn't listening to you actually. I was planning what I'd write in the church magazine.'

'But man, you must have been listening. You said something in reply.'

'Bluff!' he grinned. 'Pure bluff. Don't take everything a vicar says too seriously.'

Wednesday 14 October

Letter from one of Matthew's friends, another priest.

'Once you've given your resignation, it's like having a terminal illness,' he wrote. 'Everyone suddenly stops taking you for granted. They realise their time with you is limited, and they'll tell you all the things they've always wanted to say but somehow never dared.'

Monday 19 October

Letter from Chrystal saying that she and Duncan were delighted to hear about our move.

She referred to the *Rectory Pew* label Matthew had

described in his letter. 'Little do they know you, Jane, if they think you'll sit there!' she wrote.

Tuesday 20 October

Letter from Charlotte. 'That pew notice Matthew told us about,' she wrote. 'Do keep it after you've removed it. I'll buy it off you. I could use that for a bit of a laugh at our church.'

Matthew said that we could have an auction at this rate.

Wednesday 21 October

Henry phoned. He'd received my letter telling him we were moving, and commented that I probably had enough fodder from the churches we'd visited to write another book of *Confessions*. How about calling this one, *Vicar's Wife on the Run*?

I muttered non-committally. Then told him about Matthew's proposed auction.

'Oh no!' he disagreed. 'I should think it has quite a bit more value for you to put it on the door of the Rectory Loo.'

I suppose it could be quite appropriate to sit there and look up to see, *Rectory Pew*.

Saturday 24 October

Phone call from a man in the Christian publishing trade who was most concerned to know how I was.

'Fine!' I answered.

'I heard you weren't very well,' he said. 'Had a bad tummy bug or something?'

I was mystified. 'Who told you that?' I asked.

'Henry,' he said. 'Told me something about the vicar's wife with the runs'.

'Not WITH the runs!' I corrected. 'Vicar's Wife ON the Run. It was going to be a book title. I think I'd better change it if it's open to that much misinterpretation.'

Saturday 24 October

Meal at Pete and Jo's house. Pete came downstairs chuckling after putting Zachary to bed. He closed the lounge door and gave way to quiet laughter.

'I was doing prayers and Zachary started, 'Dear God. I'm very sorry for you that the dinosaurs all died when you had thought of making them.'

Sunday 25 October

Much giggling in the Family Service this morning. During the quietness between prayers a three-year-old whispered very loudly. 'Mummy, my bottom just coughed!'

To think, Jesus said that kids should be made welcome! When they make comments like that?!

The prayerful atmosphere just wasn't the same after that. Does Jesus say that that's OK? That prayers need not be separate from the crudities of daily life? No wonder He offended so many people with that philosophy.

On the other hand, what hope for us if all the crudities of daily life can be lifted by Him to the realm of prayer.

Monday 26 October

Spent the whole morning writing letters enquiring about London schools. Both children will have to move schools again after one term, poor things: Angus from middle to secondary, Philippa from primary to middle.

Felt sorry for myself having to arrange it all: letters to six schools in one morning. Resented the time immensely. By comparison, all Matthew's preparations seemed so glamorous. My bit seemed mere drudgery.

Felt increasingly pressured and cross. Knew some Christians would have prayed humbly, but I was in no mood even to speak to God. Instead, took avoiding action. Peeled the potatoes with excessive vigour. Muttered towards God while I peeled.

Gradually, into my hot-headed thinking, came the thought that God only asks us for a quiet obedience: from Matthew in his role, and me in my role.

As my whirring mind slowed, I recalled a verse from the Bible which had stood out as being very special when I'd read it with Angus last year. How could I have forgotten?

Dried my hands and looked it up again:

I will send an angel ahead of you to guard you along the way
And to guide you to the place which I have prepared for you.

(Exodus 23:20)

Wrote it out for each child. Left it on their pillows.

Felt so peaceful I couldn't understand why I hadn't wanted to pray earlier.

Apologised to God for being so far from holy.

Friday 30 October

Letter from Nellie. She'd been thinking that we'd need to know about schools in the area, so she was enclosing several prospectuses. She informed us there was to be an Open Day at one next week, at a Church of England High School, where they'd be very happy, she was sure, to meet the new Rector's Wife! If I'd like to come down and stay with her, I'd be most welcome of course.

Matthew and I discussed it and decided this Open Day sounded worthwhile. I could go down with Angus.

But I wouldn't go as the new Rector's Wife. I'd go anonymously, as a normal parent. That way, I'd be likely to find out much more.

November

November

Monday 2 November

Matthew decided that he could join Angus and myself on Thursday's trip to London, using the opportunity to meet various people within the church. Philippa was happy to go to a friend's house after school.

Tuesday 3 November

Matthew's plans to meet people informally have grown. Today after speaking on the phone to Nellie he announced that, instead of returning in one day, he will stay overnight. It seemed a good idea to hold an extraordinary meeting of the new Parochial Church Council on Thursday evening. That way, he said, he could listen to several strategic members of the church.

It sounded to me as if, instead of becoming less busy as he winds things down in Runcorn, he's actually going to become more frantic, juggling the dynamics of two parishes at once.

Thursday 5 November

Took train to London with Matthew and Angus.

Matthew and I parted with a kiss outside the

underground station. We had to go our separate ways: Matthew towards the church, while Angus and I headed for the schools.

Word of our coming seemed to have got round. At each school, if I mentioned that we were from Runcorn, the reply seemed to be, '*Oh*! Our new Rector comes from Runcorn.' Followed by the raised eyebrows, 'Are you his wife? And are you the Rector's son, dear?'

Angus squirmed.

At the last school, I thought we'd got away with being anonymous. Until, that is, I had to fill in a form. It asked for each parent's occupation.

Under *Occupation of Mother*, I considered writing a whole list. Encourager, Shoulder, Secretary, Personal Assistant, Recluse, Cook, Laundry Lady, Childminder, Junior-school Teacher, Taxi-driver, Telephonist, Psychologist. Oh yes, and Mistress.

Space didn't allow for everything. It seemed comparatively boring to put merely, writer.

Then, *Occupation of Father*. My mind swam with the vast number of words to describe what a clergyman does. Glazier. Plumber. Personnel Manager. Accountant. Social worker. Prophet. Teacher. Psychologist. Counsellor. Rep. (well, he represents God, doesn't he?).

I wrote *Rector*.

Looked at the word and thought, Nobody would understand that nearly as well as my other descriptions!

Handed the form back to the school Administrator. The moment she read it, her attitude changed. She became quite breathless.

'Oh! Not . . . the new Rector along the road?'

I nodded.

She was most reproachful. 'But you didn't tell me that was who you were!'

She rushed off to fetch the headmaster, then the deputy head, both of whom joined in the ecstasy.

I felt warmed by the warmth of such a welcome. It was nice to be treated with such honour. Did wish, however, that such obvious love and care were not reserved for those in certain jobs, but shared among everyone, as Jesus asked.

On the way out of school Angus said, 'How come so many people know who we are?'

I said, 'People talk about vicars a lot. Especially new ones. Or ones who make mistakes—the same mistakes as they make.'

We got on to the bus. Angus began again, 'Mum, will Dad be more important here than he is in Runcorn?'

I replied, 'No, Angus, he won't. It's just that he hasn't arrived here yet, which means he hasn't done anything they disagree with.'

The bus trundled along Ealing Broadway, past shops and market stalls.

Angus said, 'Why do they think Dad's *so* wonderful?'

'Partly because he is,' I replied with a smile. I couldn't wait to see him and exchange news. 'But mostly because each person hopes he's going to do what they want, so everything will be perfect.'

The bus had reached West Ealing. Angus was still chewing through his thoughts.

'But if so many people all have their own ideas for what they want, they won't be all the same?'

'That's right!' I agreed. 'And the day they stop saying that Dad is wonderful will probably be the day he pleases someone *else*, instead of them!'

Angus was most indignant. 'That's not fair!' he said.

'And that,' I replied, 'is why I could never be a vicar.'

Back to Nellie's for tea. I thanked God that Nellie didn't think twice about giving me mine in a mug in the kitchen, instead of using cups in the drawing room.

Looked at my mug and saw that it had written on it, THE BOSS.

Hoped she was not trying to infer anything.

Before returning to Runcorn, I told Nellie that I'm fairly keen to remove the *Rectory Pew* notice.

She grinned. I decided she was on my side so I went on, 'But don't do it surreptitiously before we come, will you?'

Her rising mirth allowed me to switch to Fun Mode in which I could delight in mischievous speculation.

'I mean, we could plan a little ceremony around it all, couldn't we? Like a funeral service: would that be best? And we could type out a service sheet with special words to intone as I took the screwdriver to it. 'Dust to dust . . .'

Nellie's grin was rather fixed.

'Jane,' and suddenly she looked like a church warden. 'Jane, you do realise one needs a Faculty from the Archdeacon to remove anything from a church?!'

Underground back to Euston via Paddington. While we waited on the platform a porter driving a wagon bumped his way along the platform. Angus hadn't seen it coming and nearly got mown down.

'Good grief!' he yowled, as I picked him up by the collar just in time to drag him out of the way. 'They don't give you much respect in London, do they? They just keep going their own way!'

I hoped that his generalisation was not true, and more particularly that it would not in fact apply to parish life.

It was dark by the time the train drew out of Euston. I allowed myself to be caught up in Angus' 10-year-old delight at watching bonfire night's rockets shoot up into the sky.

Wondered silently if any rockets would go up when Matthew and I arrived at his new parish. According to my initial impression, the church seemed pretty entrenched in its ancient traditions. Would they expect me to be the traditional Rector's wife? And how would they cope when they discovered that I'm not?

Matthew rang home late from London, long after both children were asleep. Went through his day telling me about it with enthusiasm until his final meeting (with the four wardens, from the two churches). At that point he said three words which spoke volumes.

'Hard for everyone.'

I suspected that this was a coded message: had things been tricky? He was being guarded because he could have been overheard. I therefore questioned him very imaginatively, such that he could reply with monosyllables yet give nothing away at his end.

As far as I could understand things, half the congregation is worried that their new Rector might change things. The other half is worried that he might not.

There seems only one consequence: that whatever Matthew does, half the congregation will be disappointed in him.

'Not me as a person,' Matthew corrected hastily. 'Me as Rector. That's different.'

I put the phone down and thought with rising panic, Oh NO! This could get out of hand. A disagreement could damage my relationship with Nellie! Here I am just gaining confidence with my first friend in the new parish, and before we even move there's a 'tricky meeting'! She may be in the 'Disappointed In The Rector' camp, and focus all her disagreement on Matthew. And just because I'm married to him, she might not like me any more!

Went to sleep with a sense of dread, thinking again of those rockets exploding.

Friday 6 November

Dreamed last night of the radio studios where I work freelance. Instead of me it was Matthew who was editing some recordings, while I stood outside waiting for him. When I went to collect him, I discovered he was having problems in there. I wanted to help but felt constrained, unwilling to threaten his manly independence.

Woke up wondering what this meant. Thought at first that it was my life that had been invaded by Matthew's new job as Rector: my relationship with Nellie had been threatened. Felt very angry about the system. Heard yet again the old saying that vicars' wives should never allow themselves to have real friends within the parish. I hate that saying and want to prove it wrong.

But can I?

Later told myself that the dream actually proves how much I help Matthew. When he gets into problems I come in and make him feel better like a loving wife. Even when he gets all the glory for doing such a wonderful job.

Well, I try.

Saturday 7 November

Met Gill. She's the neighbour who, when she felt suicidal last year, brought herself back from the brink by the thought that her husband *would* cope without her and he would feel smug at that. She didn't want to give him such an opportunity.

Told Gill that we're moving.

She said, 'Ah, come off it, Jane. We were just beginning to trust you enough to show you the other side of our front door!'

Her husband came up. He said, 'Yeah, we'll miss you, you know. Mind you, don't let it go to your head. I suppose you thought people were being friendly to you whenever they drove past waving to you with three fingers pointing down?'

Sunday 8 November

Woke at 6 am absolutely rigid with fright. Another nightmare. My worst kind—the aeroplane theme. I've always been plagued by these since childhood, where our home was under the flight path for Speke airport.

I've just thought, the new Rectory is under the flight path for Heathrow. More dread about the move.

In my dream we were on holiday, in our favourite Scottish glen: one of the most remote in Scotland. We were standing on the hill, admiring the view, when I caught sight of an eagle. Felt especially smug that I was the only one to see it, because Matthew had walked on ahead, out of earshot. He always mocks me for seeing things: whenever I point out a buzzard, he insists it's only a crow.

I was admiring the size of the eagle, and its steady progress from above the far mountains towards us, when suddenly I realised that it wasn't an eagle at all—it was an aeroplane. Was most thankful I hadn't given Matthew another opportunity to mock.

Looked again at the aeroplane and suddenly realised it wasn't alone but one of many. The longer I looked, the more I saw: all so high up that they were just dots in the sky. There were dozens; then hundreds. The sky became black with these dots. It was terrifying. They were wheeling and circling, still far away, but there was no doubt that they were menacing. I knew that their presence meant only one thing. War.

From there everything moved fast. I wanted to grab the children and haul them into a bomb shelter. But I couldn't find either the children or a bomb shelter.

Then there was a huge great roaring noise from the glen below—someone was running up the hill, shouting. The urgency in his voice told me that he, too, knew that a war was imminent.

The second time he shouted I could make out what he was saying: 'LEANNE!' Now, I knew Leanne to be the author of a book about sexuality. I thought, I didn't know she was here too; I'd have enjoyed talking to her about writing. Then thought of the man shouting for her. Decided he must want a quick counselling session before he got bombed. Concluded he must be desperately dependent on counselling!

Woke up with heart pounding. Oh, the relief of finding it was only a dream!

Realised that the great roaring noise was Matthew

snoring. Listened carefully to him and observed that each intake of breath resounded in the rhythm of 'Leanne!'

Couldn't close my eyes without seeing those menacing planes, so tried to wake myself up properly. Began to wonder if there was an interpretation. Supposed that the planes represented hordes of parishioners invading our peaceful family times.

Wished I had rescued Matthew as well as the children. Resolved that in future I shall be more vigilant in rescuing him whenever his day off is threatened by the invasion of parish work.

Went to church smiling. Forgot about the nightmare until we sang, 'The fight is o'er, the battle won'. Wondered who had won. Or was this God's own way of telling me that I needn't worry about battles in the new parish?

Monday 9 November

This is getting ridiculous. Another nightmare.

Another aeroplane, but a low-flying one this time. I was in a train to London and it flew alongside. Just before we arrived it released a mass of metal balls which rolled at high speed to destroy everything in their path.

Woke up before discovering whether or not I got hit. Wondered what a psychiatrist would say about these nightmares. Decided it's too dangerous to ask.

Later told Luke about this diary. He suggested that I might be wise to sit on it for at least 10 years before allowing it to be published. He thought the new parish might not like it.

What might they not like? That I'm human?

Wondered if Jesus ever wished his humanity had not been so public. Found myself thanking him most profoundly that, in order to come and live as a human, Jesus had emptied Himself. Tried to take in the fact that He had elected to do so as a measure of His love. Was unsuccessful.

Tuesday 10 December

After school, overheard Angus telling Philippa that she'd be lucky to survive for long in London, because there people don't wait for you to get out of their way. They just barge ahead and she'd easily get killed, he said. She believed every word. He insisted that 'he knew' because at Paddington station last week the porter had nearly mown him down.

I thought: Fancy, that's the whole of London condemned in Angus' mind, all because of one little careless moment by one person.

Then thought: Fancy, maybe people get put off church just as easily? By one little careless moment by one person (e.g. me), and that's their lifelong impression.

Dreaded more nightmares.

Evening Talked with Matthew until well past midnight. All about his choice of who will work alongside him as Team Vicar at one of the churches.

Matthew said he found my reflections very helpful. Thanked me most sincerely. Felt that rare glow of being thoroughly treasured.

Wednesday 11 November

Sure enough. Woke in night, frozen with terror. Thought: At least there was an interesting story-line to that nightmare . . . I must remember it all to write it in my diary and analyse it.

By morning, had no idea what it had been about.

It must have been so bad that my conscious mind had blocked it off.

Reminded myself that psychologists say our minds need to construct the worst scenarios and dream about them in order to prepare ourselves for reality.

Felt thoroughly prepared for the new parish.

Tuesday 17 November

Heard a whoop from Matthew in the kitchen as he read the post. My nosiness pulled me through. The letter was from Nellie. Matthew passed it across to me. In contrast to his obvious pleasure, I froze as I read:

Lots of parishioners are ordering Jane's books . . .

Worst moment of panic I've experienced yet over being an author. All those parishioners reading my books: people who don't know the real me but who will form an opinion according to what they read. They might decide they don't like me before I even arrive! They might decide they don't like their new Rector. How could I be responsible for that?

And which of my books are they reading, anyway? If it's *A Pathway through Pain* they may expect me to be too serious. If it's *Confessions of a Vicar's Wife* they might think I'm too frivolous.

Why did I ever write any books?

Is fame compatible with an enjoyment of life?

I read on: *. . . Matthew, you're only coming as Jane's husband you know!!*

That made me chuckle. It's about time the tables were turned, instead of me only ever being seen by parishioners as Matthew's wife. Or even less personally, as 'The Vicar's wife'.

Was Nellie trying to shrink Matthew's ego?

Did she feel she needed to?

Nellie then went on to pay one of the loveliest compliments about my book of modern-day Psalms.

Decided it was time I thanked God once again for giving me the words to write those books.

Wednesday 18 November

Not a sound from Matthew's study all day. Decided to investigate. Found him ensconced in his chair, absolutely glued to a book. Knew it must be extra-good if it kept him so enthralled.

Asked him about it. 'Excuse me,' I said, 'You OK? You don't usually read for so long when you're working.'

He didn't reply. Merely gave an absent sort of grunt. I bent down in order to peer at the book title:

A Handbook for Churchwardens and Parochial Church Councillors.

'Hello, what IS this?' I asked again.

He muttered something about having got a bit rusty after seven years in an Ecumenical church, and needing to brush up on all the rules of the Church of England. The new parish was strongly traditional.

I looked over his shoulder at the bit he was so glued to. The chapter was entitled, *Powers and Duties*.

Thought? Is it a power game between vicars and church wardens, then?

Pursued my quest to comprehend at least a little. 'Isn't this all dreadfully boring and bureaucratic?' I asked.

He looked up at me for the first time. (Major triumph for womankind there Jane! I told myself).

'It's essential,' he answered dryly. It sounded rather serious.

Then, in his 'I'm Being Interrupted' voice (oops, less of a triumph after all), he explained that it was about who has the power to do what in a church. And more relevantly, who had the power to *veto* what?

Matthew followed this explanation by a knowing nod, tongue pushed into one cheek (try it).

Had the distinct impression that this was indeed, very serious. Decided to retire quietly from his study.

After tea, while Matthew was washing up, I crept into his study to look at this mysterious book. Felt very naughty trespassing in the hallowed ground of his study.

Hastily scanned the contents. It all looked ghastly; beyond me. All, except for one line: Chapter 8, Section 2, Subsection (c). *Allocation of seats.*

Decided I must read that some time. There might be laws surrounding that ancient institution, *The Rectory Pew.*

Thursday 19 November

Group here learning 'Pastoral skills'. Not from Matthew. This course is run by two graduates in counselling who now work full-time for the diocese.

I have nothing to do with the meeting. (Unless they secretly watch me and learn how *not* to be skilled pastorally?) I don't even make the drinks at the end: I've shown them where everything is and they make themselves at home. I don't cultivate unnecessary dependence.

At the end of their meeting Matthew and I joined them for the drinks. This time the conversation revolved entirely around how they would choose the new vicar when Matthew's gone. How could they be sure of getting a good one?

Possible strategies that I recall being bandied around the room:
1. Phoning the vicar they fancy having. Anonymously. Ask him if he's thought it might be time for him to go from his present parish?

2. I said that might be a bit obvious. My experience of men—vicars especially—is that they have much more conviction about matters which they think were their *own* idea. I suggested, therefore, that they could make abusive phone calls to their choice of candidate, pretending to be his parishioners. Then he'd decide for himself that he didn't want any more of that, and apply for a move.

3. Sarah liked the principle, but thought that after a while you could add more, in suitably spiritual language. Such as, 'The Lord has led me to say to you, 'Runcorn'. Does this mean anything to you?'

4. Tessa, the psychologist who leads the group, said she has a booklet newly produced by this diocese, entitled *When Your Parish Needs a New Vicar*. Said that she puts it on the top of all the notes she carries to PCC meetings. Then she keeps dropping the notes on the floor in front of the vicar, such that he's bound to pick them up for her. So far, though, someone else has always picked it up first.

That caused Matthew to remember that a year ago he received a letter about the Church of England Appointments Procedure. When he'd passed it on to his church warden, she hadn't been surprised at all . . .

Tuesday 24 November

10 am Bumped into the Reverend William Charles Waldegrove-Smythe. He was wearing his black cassock as usual. Very courteously he asked me what I thought of Matthew's new parish.

I answered, 'The parish must be kind towards vicars' wives. The wives of the two previous vicars have stayed on there: that has to be a good sign.'

William Charles drew himself up to his full 6'6" height and stroked the chest of his cassock. He inhaled slowly through his nose, regarding me deeply.

With solemn eyes he observed, 'Jane, I must correct you. You must stop saying 'Vicar'. In your new parish Matthew will be called The Rector. And I should point out that, if you have any hope of surviving— not merely as vicar's wife, but as The Rector's Wife— you will have to remember that distinction. In fact,' and he clasped his hands together just beneath his chin in the inimitable way of a high churchman, 'I would consider that you really will have to change your whole image.'

Have to?

As I stood before him I knew at once that my trouble is, the minute I hear phrases such as 'Have to', my natural rebellious tendencies come to the fore.

At 10.03 my natural rebellious tendencies came to the fore.

But I resisted hitting him.

Wednesday 25 November

Trying to complete some Bible-reading notes. The publisher asked twelve months ago for me to finish them by the end of November.

That's FRIDAY!

Still uninspired. Irritable all day. Shouted at the children for not helping me after school. Shouted at Matthew for helping with the wrong thing. Arrived late at the parish prayer meeting and sat in a silent sulk. Became peeved that nobody noticed.

Thursday 26 November

Still irritable. Resolved that if I was going to finish the Bible-reading notes it's no use waiting for God to inspire me. Nothing for it but to sit and slog.

Sat and slogged at my desk for two hours. Progress was negligible. Spent more time developing my resentment that nobody last night had noticed how I felt. Did they think Matthew gives me 'pastoral care' just 'cos I'm married to the vicar?

Hear the letter-box and dashed to look for interesting post. (Any excuse not to slog.) Found a scruffy paper bag containing something or other. No card. No letter. Just tatty writing on the outside:

> Jane. Everybody knows chocolate is the food of the mind. You'll get them Alive to God notes sorted no probs and they'll be ace OK. Love and prayers and chocolate bars. Sandy.

Inside was my favourite, expensive chocolate.

Nearly wept. How can I bear the wrench of leaving people like that? Real Scousers who say what they feel, no messing. Their brash exterior doesn't give a clue to the tenderness within.

That bar of chocolate acted as the best inspiration possible. Posted the manuscript at 5 pm.

Friday 27 November

Woke feeling very pleased with myself at having worked so hard that I'd reached my deadline with the Bible-reading notes. Lay with smug smile before getting up.

While taking my shower, realised that I was more pleased with myself than thankful to God. I'd been peeved that He hadn't 'done something' to help; but hadn't Sandy been His messenger? Some would say, His angel, acting on His behalf.

Apologised to Him. Thanked Him for cleaning the inside of me.

December

December

Tuesday 1 December

Phone call at 8 am! Answered it silently, muttering things which I ought not to mutter. Directed all nasty thoughts against parishioners.

'Yes?'

The caller gave her name. Sounded like an enquiry about a baptism. I replied with monosyllabic, 'Yes?' again, as if daring her to go on.

Suddenly recognised the name: she's our next door neighbour in the new parish. Help! And I'd sounded so gruff!

Immediate infusion of warmth to my voice, apologies, welcoming her call.

Listened to my enthusiastic, 'Oh, it's *you*!' Asked myself why the difference in tone for new parishioners? Is this some attempt to impress them? If so, I told myself, it's a sham. I'm a sham.

Depressed all day.

Phoned Nellie in the evening. Told her about this morning's call, and about my suspicion that I must be trying to impress.

She was very nice. Forgiving. Told me I mustn't get bogged down in the grot: there is also a better side of me. I felt better.

Looking forward to moving nearer Nellie, very, very much.

Thursday 3 December

First carol singers of the season. They had a very hopeful gleam to their eye as I opened the door. The gleam spoke of their assumption, that the Vicarage will be a soft touch, guaranteed (a) to be kind and (b) to give generously.

I wondered how many people know how much a vicar earns?

I suggested they could come back a week before Christmas.

Closed the door with a sinking feeling. Since Jesus ate with tax-collectors, he would probably have been nice to money-grabbing carol singers. Aren't they a modern-day equivalent?

Sunday 6 December

Woke early when Matthew slipped downstairs for his usual early Sunday morning pray. Felt sleepy and resentful at being woken. Switched on Radio Merseyside. They were talking about me!

Immediately became wide awake. *Me*! Being talked about as having had a 'significant impact' on the first 50 years of that local radio station. Glowed with swollen pride.

Their particular conversation about me concluded with an announcement that I'd be beginning a new series of *Confessions of a Vicar's Wife* next month. I felt very much wanted. Waltzed downstairs oozing the confidence of a mega-star.

Told Matthew as soon as he'd finished his pray. Tried to sound laid back to allow space for him to leap up and kiss his famous wife.

Matthew merely grunted and put in his next spoonful of porridge.

Nothing like being put in one's place.

Monday 7 December

Met a fan.

It was at the curate's house. The fan said, 'Ooh, how wonderful to meet you.' (I wished, after yesterday, that Matthew had heard that comment.) She went on to say nice things about my books.

'But tell me, Jane, how do you manage to be such a marvellous rebel, and get away with it?'

I was about to reply that it just comes naturally when out of the corner of my eye, I noticed her husband cowering as if he hoped I would not give her any clues.

'I mean,' she went on, 'I enjoyed your books because they aren't holy are they? More—sort of—Godly, really.'

Her comment immediately enabled me to put last June's interviews into perspective. That church north of Southampton had seemed so pious. If our impression was correct, they would have wanted to squash out my voice, my down-to-earth comments. I would never have fitted. They could have resented me. And I could have resented them back.

Silently I thanked God that Matthew hadn't been appointed there. Which caused me to smile wryly. It seemed such a short time since my prayers had consisted almost entirely of pleas to let us go there.

Added my thanks that God *doesn't* answer every prayer. He rules OK!

Tuesday 8 December

Phone call from the producer at Radio Merseyside. Profuse apologies that he had been remiss on Sunday by announcing on air that I would be beginning my new series, without checking with me first.

I confessed I'd been so flattered that I hadn't noticed.

He found that very funny.

Does he think flattery will serve him well with me?

Huh.

Wednesday 9 December

Received a party invitation from Gill and Rory. Written as a limerick:

> There was a young family from Hoole
> Beginning to think about Yule
>   They were feeling quite hearty
>   So called for a party
> And hoped for food better than gruel.
>
> [RSVP by limerick]

Sat and looked at the list of Christmas cards to be written. Knew we'd never have time to sit and make up a limerick brilliant enough to represent us. That would take ages! It had to be a spur-of-the-moment job or nothing. So, as we sat opening the post, we got our heads together and wrote:

> A dashing young man who is vicar
> With his wife—who's so famed, he could kick 'er!
>   Will come to your soirée
>   Before they move far away
> And drown all their sorrows in liquor.

Matthew hoped they'd get the point and order enough booze. He loathes arriving at a party to find that it's decent booze for everyone else, fruit juice offered to clergy in case they're teetotal.

Thursday 10 December

Phone call from Gill and Rory after receiving our limerick. They wanted to assure us that they were changing their calculations for wine at their party. For everyone from their own church they'd reckoned two glasses of wine each. For Runcornians, four.

Friday 11 December

Evening More carol singers. Asked them to come back in Christmas week and NOT BEFORE.

Saturday 12 December

Matthew's birthday. This year, it's fallen on his day off. So we threw our walking boots into the car, piled in and drove off to Wales for a day on the hills. Climbed to a view, made patterns with our breath in the cold air, skimmed ice on frozen ponds, drank hot cocoa admiring remote whitewashed farms in the valleys below, and enjoyed being reminded of Scotland.

Succeeded in feeling right away from everything and everyone. Felt restored enough to cope with the knowledge that his birthday heralds an uncomfortable fact: the whirlwind of Christmas has begun. From now on, Matthew will basically be zooming around from one service to another, one visit to another, including homes, schools, hospitals, hospice, and (occasionally) parishioners.

Sunday 13 December

Wore my mini-skirt to church. In the name of research into The Christian Reaction to Fashion.

During coffee time after the service I was chatting with Fred. Tom came up to us both, grinning broadly. He gave a huge wink and, in his inimitable Lancashire accent he said, 'Keep up the good works, Jane!'

Fred dropped his cup into his saucer with an unsteady clatter.

Tom went on, his philosophical mode somehow enhanced by his Lancashire accent, 'It's great, ain' it, Fred? I mean, you could never say she's the usual vicar's wife is she?' His moustache was twitching at each end. 'I've been sitting behind her in that mini-skirt all morning, telling meself to keep me mind on things above, but it's not as simple as that ye know . . .'

I decided that another parishioner needed me. Urgently.

Concluded I must have been right not to have worn the mini-skirt to Matthew's interviews. He might never have been offered the job.

Monday 14 December

Matthew went to the refuge for battered wives with boxes of Christmas presents from the church Gift Service yesterday. As he was going out of the front door, I called after him that I'd chuck in a few old clothes which Angus and Philippa had outgrown. I moaned about their over-crowded wardrobes.

An hour later he returned a different man. He'd had the most enormous welcome from the warden. They'd been in desperate need, especially of clothes. A woman with six kids had arrived last night, bringing nothing at all. Nothing. No clothes except what they stood up in, and three of the kids had been car-sick over those, on their journey from Bolton. The kids had come in and said, 'Hey look, Mom! There's a radiator here. D'you think it'll work?' They couldn't take in the fact that that place was like a palace

compared with their previous home where their Dad was always drunk.

The warden had thanked Matthew profusely, especially for the clothes. She said no one else remembered them at Christmas time.

When Matthew told me, I could only think of my attitude to our over-crowded wardrobes and I felt almost sick.

Went to sleep praying God would forgive the meagreness of our giving.

Tuesday 15 December

6 pm   More carol singers. With vicious-looking dog (presumably to terrorise us into giving enough). Boys chewing gum stood menacingly behind.

I asked who they were collecting for. Silly question. Themselves of course. They needed new computer games.

Needed!

I thought, This is a bit rich after yesterday.

So I told them. Told them all about the kids in the refuge with nothing in the world except sicked-on clothes. Suggested they might like to collect for them.

Water off a duck's back. Why did I bother?

Pretty depressed.

Wednesday 16 December

If I answer the door to one more group of boys singing 'We wish you a merry Christmas' I think I'll scream.

Thursday 17 December

Heard canned music outside churning out the most ghastly commercialised 'carols'. It was like an ice-cream van, only there was a dressed-up Father Christmas with plastic reindeer stuck precariously on top.

I yelled for Angus and Philippa to go and hide while I rushed to switch out all our lights. I've never moved so fast in all my life.

We sat in the dark at the back of the house and I told them the story about 'the people who walked in darkness'. They were oblivious of my uncharitable spirit and innocently relished the story.

I tried to repent. Told God I felt driven to this sort

of thing. Asked Him what on earth He would have
done if He felt like me about carol singers?

As I asked Him, I had a faint suspicion that
maybe every Sunday He could run away from our
'canned' type of pseudo-worship; but He doesn't. He
graciously accepts, out of love.

At that point I could repent. Asked Him to cause
more love to well up within me.

Sometimes I ponder the fact that my life is
supposed to reflect God. Really, my mirror is very,
very mucky.

Friday 18 December

Christmas card this morning addressed to:
   The Vicar's Wife and The Broadcaster's Husband.
Wondered what on earth the postman must have
thought.

Saturday 19 December

Gill and Rory's party.
   Arrived to find a limerick at the front door:

The Millers would like you to knock
We'll offer you glasses of hock
   So be hale and hearty
   And come join the party
But please leave before one o'clock!

Then a second verse where we hung up our coats:

The children are now fast asleep
From them we shall hear not a peep
   We'll drink up some wine
   And have a good time
And then all collapse in a heap.

I'd never been to a limerick party before. On every
door were pinned more verses from guests' replies.
For example:

Our thanks go to Rory and Gill
(Their party should be really brill!)
   At present, our plan
   Is to bring a cheese flan
Prepared by our cook with great skill.

And a novel way to decline any invitation:

The Hockleys (tra-la, tra-la-tum!)
Though fond of your parties (yum yum!)
   By a sorry arrangement

Have a prior engagement
And are sadly unable to come!

Sunday 20 December

Family service in church. The place was absolutely buzzing with people, children on the floor at the front. The atmosphere was wonderful: kids totally involved up at the front, parents feeling relaxed (in church!) and enjoying themselves, as well as watching their little darlings.

Half way through the service I was struck by what a difference there was since our first Christmas here. Hardly anyone in church, then, and they relied exclusively on their new vicar for everything. Now, all that's been reversed: Matthew was off elsewhere leading a second service in the equally full school nearby.

I was looking at the fruit of seven years' ministry— and realised that we were about to drive away from it.

Very, very nearly cried.

Monday 21 December

Met Pete who asked, 'D'you know why kettles are lonely?'

I looked unusually blank.

'Zachary asked me after his Sunday School yesterday. How should I have replied?'

I could see the twinkle in Pete's eye.

'No idea,' I said. 'Why did Zachary think kettles might be lonely?'

'Because in Sunday School they'd been singing 'Away in a Manger'. And Zachary says that verse two begins, 'The kettles are lonely . . .'

Sunday Schools have a lot to answer for.

Tuesday 22 December

Overheard Matthew telling someone that he's convinced about one aspect of heaven. There will be NO Christmas carols there.

And he's always been out when the carol singers have come here!

Wednesday 23 December

Card this morning addressed to:

The Rev Matthew Grayshon and The Revered Jane Grayshon.

Thursday 24 December

9 am   I've got up early to steal a moment of peace, alone with God. It's so hard to find in this season. We've made a pagan festival so far removed from peace.

Matthew will have three Christingle services this afternoon. Communion tonight. Bed at 1.30 am then up early in the morning for more communions.

My job—my sole job—is to keep the show on the road on the home front. Lord, let me do it for You.

11 am Phone call. My editor, Henry. Someone interested in ME! Little did he know how woo-able I was by anyone who, instead of making me into a parish errand-girl, showed interest in me.

He asked about my next book. Seemed very caring. (However, I can never speak to him without the memory of that famous peanut rather blocking my concentration.) (Henry once admitted to a similar problem.)

During today's phone call I vowed silently that I must obliterate such a memory.

Told Matthew over coffee about Henry's invitation for me to fax part of my manuscript, now. Matthew said I must go for it! Downed his coffee and raced off with the manuscript himself, to the nearest fax machine: the office of Rev William Charles Waldegrove-Smythe.

Came home feeling very pleased with himself. Huge hugs and kisses. As we held each other in the kitchen, Matthew said, 'I left young William Charles reading the bit about himself.'

Sudden and total dismay. Immediate end to the hug. Horrified exclamation: 'You WHAT?'

'I said, I left William reading the bit about himself. I pointed out which one was him. Well, he would never have identified himself otherwise. I asked him if he liked the pseudonym.' He looked at my fingers going white as they gripped the kitchen cupboard.

'Wasn't I supposed to do that, lady?' he asked, using his favourite endearment.

Men are incredible.

I said nothing. Forced a smile, but decided that the time had definitely come to pour myself a mug of claret.

Through gritted teeth I thought, It's a good job I love my husband.

11.30am Henry phoned back. Had read the fax. And he likes it! So the next book is on. I was so excited I skipped and danced around the house. Forgave Matthew and resumed the hugs. Children thought it was huge fun. Fortunately, so did Matthew.

That contract will mean we can go away on holiday next year.

Evening Glowed my way through the day. Energised by my good news, I happily did my vicar's wife 'bit' with Matthew: listened to him, enthused with him, sympathised with him, answered the phone for him, fed him.

Also found time to play Monopoly with the children, play carols on violin and piano with them; wrapped and delivered last-minute presents, prepared children's stockings after they'd gone to bed, set tomorrow's table and—my regular Christmas Eve job—mopped the kitchen floor.

Stood in church at the (packed) Christingle service thinking how good it was to feel fulfilled. It made me feel so strong! Was sure I could have stooped down and helped anyone in need.

Immediately thought, But that's not how God helps us. When He stooped down to us, He didn't come with strength. He emptied that out, and became weak; as dependent as a babe.

Decided I must remember this, next time I felt useless. That's how Jesus was in the crib. Apparently, useless.

Stunned by God's nature.

Friday 25 December

Early start, of course, with children hugely excited. After opening stockings, straight to Family Service: promised children we'd open other presents immediately afterwards.

In church there was a lovely atmosphere. Children came out to the front one by one carrying their favourite present which was held up for all to admire. Several little ones wanted to stay all together at the front, gathered round on the kneelers encircling the sanctuary.

In the final hymn a little girl Sian, aged 2, tried to walk down the steps back to her parents. Lost her balance. Looked around for the nearest thing to hold on to and steady herself. Found another little girl's hair which suited her purpose very well. Grabbed it and kept tight hold as she stepped down and walked away. I shielded my ears waiting for the scream: but the little girl didn't seem to notice!

Back home opening the Christmas presents, Matthew fell asleep. The children complained that this happens every year.

Saturday 26 December

Slobbed all day.

Matthew prepared services for tomorrow.

Sunday 27 December

In church, Christine came over to speak. She's the lady who once commented how nice Mothering Sunday must be for me, because my husband always remembers Mothering Sunday by giving flowers to everyone.

Today she gave a huge sigh. 'Oh, my husband's

been so busy working up to Christmas, I've hardly seen him.'

I sympathised.

'It must be great for you, having your husband around at home all day. It must be such a help for you.'

Wondered if it was silly to expect vicarage life to be understood.

Philippa came home singing 'Once in Royal David's City'. Very sweet. Until I heard the last line: 'Christ is bored in Bethlehem.'

I was about to tell her that she was singing the words incorrectly, that her version wasn't true, when I asked myself, But *is* it true? Perhaps Christ *is* bored being stuck (in people's minds) as a baby in Bethlehem? After all, the reason for His birth was in order that He should grow up, and die, and be raised to new life.

Did not correct Philippa. Concluded that her version is more thought-provoking than the normal one.

Monday 28 December

Matthew opened his post.

'Ah, the recession has hit,' he said, peering into one envelope.

I raised my eyebrows in question.

'No whisky from the undertaker this year,' he rued. 'Just this'.

He pulled out a one-page, no-picture calendar in a plastic folder. The name of the funeral director was written in large red letters across the top.

This year's present didn't go down quite so well as last year's.

Tuesday 29 December

Met Rachel. She was bursting with giggles about something or other.

'Must tell you about the visitors staying with us over Christmas,' she said.

I listened attentively.

'One of them had been given your *Confessions* as a present, so he's been reading it at our house. About halfway through he looked up and asked me, 'This Rachel person Jane Grayshon writes about—d'you know her?'

Rachel gave another giggle.

'By the end of the book, he said, "It's not *you* is it?"'

She looked very pleased to have been identified. And so relieved to be seen with shortcomings instead of idolised as if she should be sinless.

Perhaps our church should put one of those big posters outside church saying, *Church is for sinners.* Underneath, Rachel and I could add, *The ministers and their wives are sinners too.*

But then, what might the Bishop think of that?

Perhaps he would feel impelled to add, *So is the Bishop.*

Wednesday 30 December

Went away for a couple of nights. Stayed with friends we've known for some years. At their church a new vicar was appointed 16 months ago.

No sooner had we arrived than we met a stalwart member of the church. She leaned into the car to chat, telling us about their 'new' vicar.

I thought, How long does a vicar have to be in a parish before he stops being referred to as 'new'?

They do say that a clergyman has a year of being considered wonderful, a year of being considered abysmal, and by year three he begins to be seen as the person he really is.

Anyway it was clear that the honeymoon period for this 'new' vicar was certainly over.

'He's not the same,' this dear lady was saying, her head shaking disapprovingly. She drew out her words, dwelling on their importance. 'Nothing's the same any more.'

She looked very downcast.

I felt very sorry for anyone who has the job of being a new vicar. Anywhere.

Thursday 31 December

Met many more friends from the church. Heard many more comments about the 'new' vicar.

The ultimate seemed to be, 'He's really changed the vicarage! You wouldn't recognise it!'

Was unsure whether such remarks were compliments or complaints. Or were they neither? Were they simply something to talk about?

With every comment, my mind flitted to Matthew's new parish in London. I thought, This time next year, everyone will be going through the same conversations with their visiting friends. Perhaps their complaints will be exactly the same! Certainly the tone of voice: just a hint of scandal.

Will I be able to stop myself from taking it personally? To remember that it's Matthew the Rector they're talking about, not Matthew the person?

Evening Before the New Year's Eve party, talked quietly with Matthew about all these people we've met so far here, blithely blaming the new vicar for whatever is less than good in their church.

'That's OK,' said Matthew. 'That's part of the job specification of any vicar, to be blamed for what's not necessarily his fault.'

He seemed so calm!

'I just have to accept it,' he said. 'Otherwise I'm paralysed.'

Then he added, 'Which is exactly what many people would like.'

I do NOT find this easy. It all sounds ominously as if there could be tension ahead, which I'd hate.

Thanks to that discussion and Matthew's quiet serenity, I managed to put all fears aside. Had a great party!

January

January

Friday 1 January

Woken by an aeroplane nightmare. (What a way to begin the new year! Do parishes have any idea of how their clergy feel about things?)

This one was dominated by the terrible noise the aeroplane made in its dying moments. I had been on a hill with a vast panoramic view, and had had to watch the plane spluttering along, knowing it was about to either explode in mid-air or sink to the earth and land: possibly on top of all of us standing helplessly in its flight path.

Woke before discovering which it did.

Tried to calm myself down. Rationalised that coming here and hearing about their new vicar had brought to mind all the tensions of new vicars. The possibility of things crashing in total failure.

Told myself it's only a possibility; not to worry.

Wished everyone a happy new year. And they wished me one.

Saturday 2 January

Family party. The extended family. All on best behaviour. All succeeded in showing their nicest side:

we were four nice families, with our nice Granny, all showing how well brought up our children are.

After lunch Zachary plodded in to where all the adults were sitting quietly after coffee. He placed his beloved tractor on the carpet and began to push it along. He made the tractor's slow chugging sound.

'Bugg-er Bugg-er Bugg-er . . .'

His parents looked as if they wished to die.

'It's *ch*ugger *ch*ugger *ch*ugger—' Pete tried to get through to his son.

'Bugg-er Bugg-er Bugg-er . . .'

Sunday 3 January

Matthew began to get the same bug as I've had all last week. A cold. Only now Matthew's got it, he's announced that it is flu.

Typical man!

Monday 4 January

Phone call from people we'd stayed with over the New Year. Stark news. Amanda, the 10-year-old daughter of friends there, died this morning.

Matthew had answered the telephone and he sat numbly holding the receiver when he was told. I went to the other telephone but there was nothing to hear really. Just numbness to share. The inability to take it in; the impossibility of imagining that pretty little body, so full of life, now dead.

We distracted ourselves by talking about the funeral. Thursday. It seemed profane somehow; so earth-bound at a time when all thoughts are towards heaven. At least we know that that's where Amanda is. No guess work: we know.

I told Angus before he went to sleep. Having gone to playgroup with Amanda many years ago, he too found the news hard to believe.

'Agi,' we remembered together her endearing way of pronouncing Angus' name when she first talked. She had had such a soft voice.

God, why have you taken her away? Why one so lovely?

Tuesday 5 January

Couldn't bring myself to tell Philippa about Amanda when she woke. Thought she'd cry a lot, as she did a month ago when I first told her that this was a possibility.

Went through the morning sort of watching myself; not thinking about what I was doing but about Amanda and her family. Kept seeing her bright eyes and her beautiful smile; kept imagining them becoming dulled by death. Oh, all those children I'd nursed through this stage! Not Amanda too, Lord!

Heard myself let out a moan, longing for her. No tears, though. The grief was too deep to come out yet. And no prayers either. Apologised to God; but I felt too numb to verbalise anything. The moan was the nearest to a prayer. God would have to accept that.

Gerty called. Brought my shopping, as she's been doing twice a week for seven years since she knew how ill I'd been.

When she arrived I stood in silence as she carried the stuff in. Only when she reached the kitchen did I find my voice to speak.

'Amanda died yesterday morning.'

It must have sounded very stark.

Gerty just opened her arms to give me a big hug.

Gerty's not the most demonstrative of people, so that hug meant a lot. It gave me permission to shed a first tear. But it wasn't big enough to spill over. When she stopped, it was Gerty's cheeks which were wet.

Truly, Gerty knew how to weep with those who weep. She was a friend more than a parishioner. And whatever anyone says, all vicars' wives need friends.

After school, plucked up the courage to tell Philippa as we walked home. She took it completely in her stride!

'Well, we did *pray* that Amanda would be made better. And now she is!'

I looked at her in amazement. Couldn't even reply.

'Isn't she, Mummy?!' It was more a statement than a question. 'She'll be having a lovely time with Jesus.' She skipped happily alongside me, holding my hand as we walked. 'I wonder if *she*'s allowed to play with make-up in heaven?'

I ignored the bait. It seemed more important to consider which was the more appropriate reaction to the news: Philippa's light-heartedness or my sombre heaviness?

A few paces further on she asked more pensively. 'Mummy, in heaven, are people the same age as when they died? I mean, d'you get older there?'

I could only reply that I didn't know, but she could ask Daddy. There are at least some occasions when I'm glad that the local vicar is so close at hand that I can refer the awkward questions to him.

Wednesday 6 January

All waking time taken up thinking of Amanda's family. Couldn't concentrate on any work. Tried to busy myself doing practical things. Decided that the best distraction would be to defrost the freezer before the removal.

Found several unmarked bags. Became exceptionally irritated by that: well, by Matthew doing it. He gets people admiring him for being so domesticated as to decant stuff into bags (what *I*'ve cooked, NB) and put it into the freezer, but the doting parishioners don't notice that he hasn't labelled it. And then I come to the freezer and haven't a clue what half the stuff is.

At lunchtime, Matthew came in and I told him. Silently, in a sort of mime, so he'd realise for himself what was wrong. I stood with my toe tapping on the floor, holding out the unlabelled plastic bags one at a time.

Each one was an unidentifiable white solid mass.

'Oh, don't worry!' Matthew said in his I'm - Not - Going - To - Be - Bowed - down - By - Anything - You - Say voice. 'That's—let's think—ah yes, that's apple in there. I remember puréeing it.'

He pulled one of the bags from my outstretched hand. He beamed his extra specially reassuring smile.

'We'll have puréed apples for pudding tonight,' he said, transferring the solid mass to a saucepan.

I gave a silent nod, but my eyebrows were still raised in question, thus making sure I did *not* look reassured.

5 *pm* From my study window, caught sight of Matthew walking down to the bottom of the garden with saucepan. He had a skulking look to him.

By the time he came back into the kitchen I was standing there waiting. I raised my eyebrows once again.

He tried to smile. 'Er, not puréed apples for pudding,' he said. Another reassuring grin, but it had become decidedly sheepish.

'I think,' he explained, holding the pan at arm's length under the running tap, 'I think that that might once have been turkey soup. But it must have been three years old. I've—er—buried it at the bottom of the garden.'

I shook my head at him in remonstration. 'It's a good job I love you', I murmured.

Suddenly we were hugging one another in a huge

181

bear hug. We had one another, and that was more important than any rotten food. I closed my eyes and thought, If only it was stale turkey soup that had to be buried this week.

Evening   Surprise visit from a couple who belong to the new parish in London. They were on holiday in Chester and decided Runcorn was close enough to drop by.

Couldn't help wondering, Were they spying out the land?

They looked terribly impressed with everything. Perhaps new parishioners look at everything their new Rector says or does through rose-tinted spectacles for a while? Certainly this couple seemed to.

Felt a very, very faithful wife that I didn't tell them that Matthew fails to label freezer bags.

Thursday 7 January

The day of Amanda's funeral.

Six hours driving altogether, for a service of a few minutes. Yet it was so important to go. Why? We talked about that in the car on the way.

Matthew said that every time he'd prayed in the last month, he'd found himself reaching for the Psalms and, almost in tears, beseeching God for Amanda's family. As we talked on, he observed that probably this situation had reawakened the memories of what it had been like for him when I was so critically ill. Now he was no longer the one with the pain of watching a loved one suffer. He was the observer. And he could see in Amanda's family the same gift which he'd been given years ago: a gift that he could not face at the time. Grace, I suppose it's called. Grace to trust, and grace to go on, just putting one foot in front of another to get through each day, each hour.

But he went on to say that somewhere in the tears was anger, too. Said he'd wanted to cry to God, 'Look, can't you see?' He needed to come to the funeral to shout that to God, along with so many others in the church.

Strangely, at the service, we were the ones ministered to. As Amanda's parents walked down the aisle, into the midst of so very many people who looked on in silent grief, her Mum in particular glowed with the quiet serenity of one whose prayer life is deep. Emanating from her to her husband and her (now) only child, was that peace which the world cannot give. It certainly passes all human comprehension.

In those few minutes of the funeral service, it was as if God were pointing to her and whispering to us, 'Look, can't you see?'

Friday 8 January

Phoned Nellie to tell her I'm coming to London next week, and asked if I could drop by?

She sounded SO thrilled to hear me, she nearly bowled me over.

Then she talked about the actual move. Said she'd been doing her duty as church warden, writing out the church rota for who's preaching on which Sunday during the interregnum. For the first time Matthew's name appears for his first Sunday, 21 March.

She said, 'It's AWFULLY near!'

Didn't like her choice of the word 'awfully'. I mean, she could have said beautifully near, or wonderfully near; but awfully?

Slight sense of foreboding.

Evening Went to the annual clergy party which everyone considers to be duty.

Kept trying to stop myself thinking, 'Oh good grief, only clergy would do THAT!' For example, no sooner had we entered than all the men huddled together in a circle discussing Christmas presents from undertakers. And I looked at myself with a group of other women, all being so immaculately polite to one another that we didn't seem to say anything significant.

As we sat down to eat the delicious food, two clergy began talking about how many weddings they each had. Somehow that was a final straw. I interrupted them—actually stopped them talking!—to say, 'Excuse me, this is *meant* to be a party!'

They looked bemused and bewildered. So I explained, 'We're supposed to socialise! And you're just talking shop all the time!'

Immediately felt guilty. They're very nice men. If that's what they wanted to talk about, who was I to object? I'd spoiled things for them now. Brought an awkwardness. It would have been much more comfortable if I'd just let things be.

Met 'the new curate' and his wife, who have moved to about 8 miles away. Like a breath of fresh air they were. They'd spiked and moussed and waxed their hair until it stood as stiff as a poker; they both wore ear-rings, and her lycra leggings (the sprayed-on variety) contrasted strongly with the floral dresses and bows of many clergy wives.

'I say,' she whispered. 'Once you get to be vicar, is it a rule that every vicarage has to have at least three pictures of churches hanging in their lounge?'

I cringed. We have one. Help—are Matthew and I showing first signs of conformity?!

Few people spoke to them. That made me very angry. What does that say about the millions of fashion-conscious, independent-minded people? No wonder they don't want to come into the churches if they first have to don the uniform and be moulded into the 'nice' flowery Church of England!

It transpired that 'the new curate's wife'—for that was the anonymous way to which she was referred, though her name is Naomi—is a vet. I was just getting into conversation with her about her job when the Rev William Charles Waldegrove-Smythe came into the room. He politely asked her what her work entailed.

'Shoving my arm up cows' back passages a lot of the time,' she answered with a grin.

William Charles went pale. He blinked fiercely and muttered, 'Oh, er, I see,' and sat down on the far side of the room, next to his wife. He needed her comfort as Naomi went on to describe her work in fuller detail. Suffice it to say, some of her tales were even more colourful than my stories from the infertility clinic, and I consider that mine are unrepeatable.

Yes, the party conversation would definitely have been safer if the clergy had been left to talk about weddings and funerals.

As we all made our farewells, Naomi landed Rev William Charles Waldegrove-Smythe a huge smack of a kiss. Said she couldn't resist it to see his face.

His face showed an expression of total disbelief and confusion.

Saturday 9 January

Dinner at Gill and Rory's home. A farewell 'do'! A wonderful evening.

Other guests included a dentist. I don't think I've ever met a dentist socially before. Most disconcerting it was. It made me uncomfortably aware of my own teeth: especially when he said how many people tell him they clean their teeth twice a day but he can see quite clearly that they don't.

I kept licking over my teeth hoping he wasn't judging my brushing of them.

On the other hand, the tales this dentist told were refreshingly unusual. Like the lady who'd come to him the week before Christmas having lost her false teeth. This was 'an emergency'—she couldn't find them anywhere. Could he give her something to wear during the festive season?

He did, and had seen her again on 6 January. 'I've found them!' she'd announced before she'd even entered his surgery, positively rejoicing.

'Where?'

'When I was taking all my decorations down, they fell out of the tree. They must have been in its branches all through Christmas time!'

I thought this story begged many questions. How had the teeth got there in the first place? And what had all the people who visited her thought as they had sat looking at her Christmas tree, and seen her teeth? Why had they said nothing to her? Had they imagined that she had *deliberately* perched her teeth in the tree as a different style of Christmas tree decoration?

Out till half past midnight. Exhausted. However, before going to bed I took an extra 10 minutes brushing and flossing my teeth.

Sunday 10 January

Brushed and flossed teeth very thoroughly before church.

Evening Away preaching, jointly with Matthew. We've never done that before but I think it went quite well.

Flossed teeth carefully before going.

After the service, a lady came up to me and said, 'You're not as I'd imagined you from the radio, you know!'

The dreaded comment! I've never known whether or not to risk asking a person to explain. Was the real

live person better or worse than the disjointed voice? And whichever way round, was that a compliment?

Nosiness got the better of me.

'In what way, Different?' I asked.

'Smaller,' she said.

That was a relief.

Back home, during my teeth-cleaning session, I pondered on how different God must be from our picture of Him. We don't even hear His voice as clearly as on the radio: we only read about what He says. Our image of Him must be so distorted.

Looking forward to seeing Him!

Talked with Matthew for a long time in bed about the new parish. He's concerned about trying to run two churches on his own: he'd hoped to have appointed a curate for one church by now. With three services per morning, he'll be hard pressed yo-yoing from one venue to another, and will have no time to meet people before he has to dart off to the next service.

Monday 11 January

Woke at 6 am. Nightmare. It must stem from last night's conversation.

There was a double-decker bus which was driving along a runway. Then it took off and flew with admirable ease through the air. As an observer I could tell that the pilot must have been delighted with his progress because the bus went higher and higher from the ground.

Suddenly, the slightest little tiny wobble. Immediate descent, but it was out of control. Everything escalated and the flying double-decker bus imploded and burst into flames.

Only half woke. Wished I could wake up completely to get the image from my mind. Asked myself if I should advise Matthew not to take on a double-decker job in the new parish. He might implode.

On second thoughts, perhaps the nightmare wasn't about that. Perhaps we should never preach together again?

Thursday 14 January

Went to London for the day to sort out various practicalities of the new house and Philippa's schooling. Stayed with Nellie, who could not do too much for me. As she drove me round from one do-it-yourself shop to another I said, 'Look, I feel awful about you doing so much.'

'But WHY?' she asked, genuinely surprised.

'I'm putting you out,' I explained. 'Preventing you from doing what *you* want to be doing today.'

We had stopped at some traffic lights and Nellie turned to me.

'Jane, I want to serve you and Matthew. Lots of us do. *This* is what I want to be doing today.'

Felt warmed right through. Nellie meant it. What an honour!

Silently thought, 'Lord, may I never, never abuse the privileges attached to being a vicar's wife.'

Friday 15 January

Matthew told me he must choose the hymns for his induction service by next week.

'Oh yes?' I said. 'Have you got, *Lo he comes with clouds descending*?'

Sunday 17 January

Sermon today was about our relationship with God needing to grow deeper.

We sang the chorus, *We want to learn to appreciate you.*

Afterwards Matthew said, 'D'you think that would be a good hymn for the induction? I mean, it might give the new congregation the opportunity to affirm their intentions towards their new Rector.'

'Nonsense!' I said. 'They're all falling over each other in appreciation of you anyway. It's the Rector's wife they have to *learn* to appreciate.'

Monday 18 January

Matthew's chosen the hymns for his induction service.

He passed me his list.

The collection hymn was, *I hear the sound of rustling.*

I roared with laughter.

I said, 'So you're hoping for notes in the collection plate instead of coins, are you?'

Tuesday 19 January

All this week Matthew has arranged to spend part of each day in six of the different local schools, taking assemblies or leading discussions with some fifth formers.

Today he was just leaving one school when the deputy head bounded up to him.

'Matthew, I wanted to thank you for everything,' she said.

Matthew was speechless.

'You've done more than you'll ever know. We've really valued . . . well, not just what you've said, but the way you are. I mean, usually when a vicar comes into school, the staff cringe, and slide down their seats in embarrassment, knowing the kids are switched off by religious talk. But you're so different. We all want to thank you.'

Matthew was incredibly humble while we ate lunch together.

I rather liked it.

Wednesday 20 January

Collected the children from school. A mum came over to me and said, 'You've no idea how much we'll miss Matthew, you know.'

You could have knocked me down with a feather!

'That's very nice,' I said, warmed by her sincerity. Then, because I knew her a little, I went on to ask, 'I'm intrigued that you should say that. May I ask what you mean, that you'll miss him, since you don't know him from church?'

'You've no idea,' she said.

I decided she was right. I had no idea.

Later I told Matthew.

'I think what she's saying,' he replied philosophically, 'is that when the vicar walks through the playground it feels to her as if God's around too. That gives her a good feeling. She'll miss it: if the vicar goes away, she feels God won't be so close.'

If that's true, it's TERRIBLE!
I could never be a vicar.

Thursday 21 January

Bumped into another mum, who waxed eloquent about how wonderful Matthew is, and how everyone'll miss him.

I stood drinking in all the compliments. Agreed with them all.

Drove home wishing that people didn't wait till you're leaving before they say such nice things. It's a bit like when people think you're dying. When I was so seriously ill some years ago, and expected to die, people came and told me how much I meant to them. All the nice things they didn't dare say if I was still going to be around. I remember thinking then, Why do we have to wait till we're dying before others feel free to say how much they appreciate us? Why on earth are we so restrained in life?

Came home and gave Matthew a very big hug.

Sunday 24 January

After church I stood chatting to Tom.

'I've been thinking,' he said.

That means quite something coming from Tom.

'Oh yes?' I replied light-heartedly, mimicking what he would have said if he'd been me.

'Yeah,' he said.

'And?' I wasn't sure what was coming.

'And—well, it's not easy to say really Jane.'

I waited. Decided this was not the time to enter our usual banter.

'But, er, it's very hard for us, you know, that you and Matthew are leaving us. You're very er, special, you know. Yeah.'

I blushed.

'Thanks,' I said.

'Yeah,' he said, more to indicate that he hadn't finished yet. 'Well,' and he cleared his throat. 'You get the sort of feeling with Matthew that we'll probably turn on the telly in a few years' time, and we'll see some announcement that he's been made Bishop or summat. And we'll say, "We knew 'im. 'e used to be at our church".'

It may have been difficult for Tom to say, but it was even more difficult for me to respond.

'Go on with you!' was the best expletive I could utter.

Tom gave a knowing nod. 'We've allus known it's a privilege to 'ave Matthew and you 'ere,' he said.

Came home and began making the gravy for lunch. When Matthew returned—before it had burned, for once—I told him

He grabbed the whisky bottle from the cupboard.

'Never!' he snorted. And he poured himself a slug, and diluted it less than usual.

I think he needed it to help him over the shock.

Evening　Was pretty thoughtful sitting alone after I'd put the children to bed and before Matthew came back from the evening service. Kept asking myself, What IS this? Why are so many people suddenly saying all these nice things?

Felt strangely insecure in the light of such overwhelming warmth.

Do I really want to walk away from all this acceptance and, well, love really?

Sandy popped round after the service. She and I sat chatting on kitchen stools while Matthew and his meeting enjoyed the comfort of the lounge.

I told her about the week of compliments.

'Don't worry,' she said. 'I guess it'll be an upward curve all the way now.'

It all seemed pretty much expected, to her.

'Think of the last minister. It's five years since he left and he's achieved sainthood by now. I don't think he had it when he worked here, like, but he's certainly gorrit now.'

Before she left she said over her shoulder, 'By the way, Matthew's got to marry me when I'm ready to be married.'

Tuesday 26 January

Matthew told me he's planning the hymns for the farewell service here as we're sent out to the new parish.

I thought of all my nightmares and suggested, *You are my hiding place*.

Very politely, Matthew replied, 'I think the relevance of that may be lost on most people.'

'OK then. What about a hymn for all those who are a bit hesitant about your good points? Help them along a bit by singing, *Glorious things of thee are spoken?*'

'A bit more on the theme of departure,' he replied. '*Thou didst leave thy heavenly throne?*'

Perhaps it would be better to get the music group to choose hymns.

Wednesday 27 January

Must make sure we don't mix up the hymns for Matthew's farewell service here with the welcoming service in London.

It would be pretty awful to sing at his welcoming service, *Send me out from here, Lord*.

Thursday 28 January

New group met at the vicarage: a five-week course to learn about Transactional Analysis. Run by a very well qualified tutor who does these courses all over Chester diocese. This is the first term that I've signed up.

In her introduction the tutor said, 'Tonight's session is about stroking.'

Before she could even explain that she was using 'stroking' as a jargon word, Charles leaned forward eagerly in his seat at the end of the settee and grinned, 'Can't wait for the practical!'

Raucous laughter.

Actually, it was good once we got past the jargon. Stroking only means 'affirming'.

We all decided we need to stroke other people more often.

February

February

Tuesday 2 February

Matthew went to London for the day, for more meetings in the new parish.

I met him from the train back home. He kissed me and told me how lovely the Rectory is now that it's being redecorated.

'Except,' he said, 'the landing and stairs.'

He wore a pained expression. 'We got the colour scheme all wrong there. They look awful.'

He winced at the very thought. '*Awful*!'

Wednesday 3 February

Matthew phoned Nellie to thank her for ferrying him around yesterday. Told her the low point of the day was seeing how horrific the colour scheme looked on the landing and stairs. Told her we'd have to get it painted again.

'Oh no, please leave it,' Nellie begged quickly.

Matthew smiled down the phone. 'We couldn't possibly leave it. We took a gamble thinking those colours would look good and now we just have to accept that we made a bad mistake.'

Nellie grew quite excited. 'Precisely!' she said. 'It

would really help us parishioners if you left it like that, you know Matthew.'

Matthew expressed his confusion.

'Because then,' she explained, 'we could come to the Rectory and see that you *can* make mistakes.'

Thursday 4 February

Second week of the group learning about Transactional Analysis.

The tutor arrived and said, 'Had an awful start to my tutorial last Friday. I was doing Marriage Guidance and opened my flip chart on the wrong page. I turned to the page I'd been doing with you last week: Types of Stroking. Had terrible problems trying to explain that that was *not* part of the Marriage course . . .'

She flipped over to today's pages for us.

From the brief glimpses we had, we thought we'd like to do her Marriage Guidance course.

Reminded me of one of the consultants I used to work for when I was a Midwifery Sister. He once dived straight off from giving a lecture to medical students about reproduction, to give a talk about British flowers to his church Mothers' Union group. Both talks were illustrated by slides. In his rush he grabbed the projector and slide cartridge, thinking he'd emptied out all the slides on reproduction. Unfortunately, in his haste he'd left one in. It was the most graphic of his set, of the male reproductive organs. I gather it was the first one to appear on the screen for the Mothers' Union ladies.

One must always check one's slides and visual aids. Especially before speaking to a Christian group. They are very shockable.

Friday 5 February

Another farewell dinner in our honour. This is wonderful.

Met another vicar's wife. However, she was nice despite that. And she had a brain. And her husband encouraged her to use it.

Discussed Rectory Pews. I was offered much sympathy that our new parish has one. We discussed at length who would sit in the Rectory Pew after we remove the label? Decided it would be either very forward people, or very innocent.

The vicar's wife recalled how the simple act of sitting 'anywhere' in her husband's church, had created endless gossip, according to who she chose to sit beside. If it was someone with money, she was accused of trying to familiarise herself with them. If it was one person two weeks running, she was accused of favouritism. If she sat alone, she felt very lonely.

Seems to me that some people seem determined to gossip, and they don't mind how trivial their subject is.

When we returned home I was brushing my teeth before going to bed, and remembered how much I had brushed them last month after our dinner with the dentist. That didn't last too long! Wondered if people who met Matthew and have their spiritual conscience pricked, are equally quick to let their need for God become dulled?

Saturday 6 February

Supposed I ought to start sorting, tidying, cleaning, packing. Spent the whole day doing a 'Pre-Removal Sort-out' with the children helping.

At least, they said they were helping. They had a whale of a time peering into boxes which hadn't been opened for years, getting everything out and either reminiscing (noisily: 'Oh, *I* remember that!'), dressing up (messily, with garments strewn everywhere), or playing long-forgotten board games.

Decided that mothers need a great deal of extra patience to let their children 'help' before moving house.

Monday 8 February

Suddenly realised, it's exactly one month from today that we move. Still LOADS of sorting, tidying, cleaning, packing, to do.

Told myself not to panic!

Tuesday 9 February

Sorting, tidying, cleaning, packing.

Wednesday 10 February

Sorting, tidying, cleaning, packing.

Thursday 11 February

Sorting, tidying, cleaning, packing.
Getting tired of this.

Friday 12 February

Matthew in London since yesterday. By this morning I'd filled two sheets of A4 paper with phone messages, most of whom he had to phone back.

At 9.30 this morning it was Mrs Pinkerton.

'It's about Sunday's service,' she said breathily. 'Can Matthew phone me this evening? I need to prepare my "bit".'

'He'll be delighted . . .'

Then remembered. 'Oh—we're going out tonight.'

'I see,' she said. 'Is it his day off?'

I confessed that it was not. Was I imagining the disapproval I sensed?

Slightly apologetically, I explained, 'It's the first time we've been to the theatre together for months—if not a year.'

'That's nice,' she conceded.

She seemed to be melting slightly so I dared to go on, 'I've told him I do NOT want to be late.'

'Of course not!' I guessed she would never countenance being late for anything like that. 'So he can phone me before you go for your lovely evening out.'

'We need to leave at 6.45,' I ventured. 'He'll get back from London at about 5.30.'

'That's fine. I'll be in then. He can phone me any time for us to chat over everything ready for Sunday.'

She sounded as if she had terminated the conversation.

'Hang on!' I said. 'This means he'll only be in for about an hour!'

'Plenty of time for him to phone me!'

It sounded so simple. From the way she was talking, it seemed ridiculous for me to suggest that her request might be difficult for Matthew. One phone call to one parishioner can easily be squeezed into a whole hour of his time.

A feeling of guilt crept up my neck like a growing blush: guilt that I could not please her.

'Poor man, he's a list of several phone calls to make in that time,' I hinted.

'Mine is urgent', she pressed.

Suddenly, a rush of adrenalin gave me the courage to put Mrs Pinkerton in the picture.

'OK, Mrs Pinkerton,' I said, steadying my voice. 'I will make sure Matthew phones you. But perhaps I can help you understand if he sounds rushed. When he steps off the train, Angus and Philippa will each want at least five minutes of his attention.'

I missed out the fact that, so will I.

'. . . Then he'll have to eat, and it would be nice if we could have a family meal instead of the children and me watching him gobble everything down while speaking on the phone or fretting over his diary in order to squeeze in yet another "emergency". I have listed two pages of messages for him to deal with as soon as possible.'

There wasn't a sound from Mrs Pinkerton. Not even a cough.

'So you see, while you agreed that we shouldn't be late for the theatre, the only reason we'd be late is if the parish comes before our night out.'

Felt extremely apprehensive waiting for a response. I'd really pushed the boat out suggesting she might be 'the parish' instead of 'vicar's friend'.

When she spoke, it was to thank me. Her voice sounded unexpectedly kind. I even had the feeling that she understood.

Perhaps I should explain the pressures on Matthew more often?

Put the phone down thinking. But why should I be answerable to parishioners like this? Explaining every detail of our days before they believe that life in a vicarage is so blooming public we hardly ever see one another alone?

The guilt merely grew. These thoughts sounded highly unspiritual. Chided myself: Fancy having nasty thoughts! Fancy suggesting Matthew might not being wholly available as the nice, caring person the parish would like him to be! Wouldn't it be better for me to be considered the lovely vicar's wife who supports her husband in every way so he can always help others, instead of being the one who suggests he should give some time to his family?

Then reasoned firmly, NO! It's a fallacy to believe that Jesus was 'gentle Jesus meek and mild'. When people demanded too much of Him, He made himself unavailable. And that wasn't even at the end of His ministry, when He was tired: that was how He started out! It's in the very first chapter of Mark. The disciples told Jesus that lots more people were looking for Him, and Jesus replied, 'Let's go somewhere else!' And so He had walked away.

Few people remember that, when they're pressing their vicar for his time.

THEREFORE:

I must not feel guilty when parishioners demand
    more than we can give.

I must not feel guilty when parishioners demand
    more than we can give.

I must not feel guilty when parishioners demand
    more than we can give.

I must not feel guilty when parishioners demand
    more than we can give.

I must not feel guilty when parishioners demand
    more than we can give.

I must not feel guilty when parishioners demand
    more than we can give.

I must not feel guilty when parishioners demand
    more than we can give.

I must not feel guilty when parishioners demand
    more than we can give.

I must not feel guilty when parishioners demand
    more than we can give.

I must not feel guilty when parishioners demand
    more than we can give.

I must not feel guilty when parishioners demand
    more than we can give.

I must not feel guilty when parishioners demand
    more than we can give.

I must not feel guilty when parishioners demand
    more than we can give.

I must not feel guilty when parishioners demand
    more than we can give.
I must not feel guilty when parishioners demand
    more than we can give.
I must not feel guilty when parishioners demand
    more than we can give.
I must not feel guilty when parishioners demand
    more than we can give.
I must not feel guilty when parishioners demand
    more than we can give.
I must not feel guilty when parishioners demand
    more than we can give.
~~I must not feel guilty when parishioners demand~~
    more than we can give.
(however much they moan and complain that their
vicar isn't good enough).

Saturday 14 February

Valentine's Day today. Rather pleased with my card
to Matthew. It's great to be in love.

Matthew put his arm around me and said, 'Lady,
I'm sorry, I forgot to get you a card.'

Forgave him. Knew that his motto is that Valentine's
Day serves as a reminder to him that my birthday is
in a week. Consoled myself that he won't forget my
birthday.

Evening Thought a lot about yesterday's conclusion.
It seems to me that there's another issue, and that's a
simple question:

Do parishioners believe in marriage, or not?

And if so, will they encourage their vicar to give
time to his marriage? Or will they begrudge him that
time?

Two of our friends who are clergy have separated
recently and it's ghastly. They say it's simply because
the strain has been too much.

I remembered hearing a well-known Christian writer and speaker describe the strain on clergy marriages. She said that so many parishes advertise for a 'married man' as vicar, but that's not what they mean. They want a single man who will bring along a telephonist who'll stay in the background doing the chores like his cooking, and washing and ironing his surplices.

They don't want him to have a wife, who makes demands.

They want him to be available to fall in love with *them*, the parish. They want to woo him, give him their time, invite him to their homes for cups of tea, glasses of sherry. And they want him to respond by giving of his time, showing them his love for them, sharing his life with them. They want him to make himself available to support them whenever they need a shoulder to cry on.

They don't want him to be unavailable for them. Least of all because of another woman! That almost invariably leads to jealousy.

I laughed when I first heard things described in this way. Now I find it too true to be funny. I've seen this to be true for so many parishioners, so many vicars' wives, so many vicars themselves. It's too easy to put the parish first. Too rewarding. Too deceptive.

Prayed at length this morning. Asked God to fill this impoverished world with His love. We're like those emaciated children in pictures of famine-strewn lands; only our hollowness is waiting in desperation to be filled with the food of love.

Sunday 15 February

Matthew's final service at Beersheba Church.

Thought it might be a bit of a tear-jerker, but fortunately it wasn't.

Received a card from Mildred. They're all Mildred

205

at Beersheba but this one is the Mildred who has stayed as a child mentally.

The card was barely legible. After some time studying it at home, we deciphered GOODBYE (copied off the front of the card) and below that:

WITH WE'L MIS YU
LOVE SORY TO HER
FROM YER
MILDRED LEVING US

Realised that she'd run out of space at the bottom of the card, below 'leaving us' so had put 'with love from Mildred' in the space which remained: to the left of the rest of her message.

That is one of the most moving cards we have received.

Thanked God for special people.

Monday 15 February

Sorting, tidying, cleaning, packing.

Tuesday 16 February

Sorting, tidying, cleaning, packing.

Wednesday 17 February

Out speaking to a large group about 50 miles away.

Used the theme of the different hats I wear in life: nurse's cap, vicar's wife's hat, writer and broadcaster (headphones), and patient's cap.

Deliberated for a long time what hat to choose to depict a typical vicar's wife.

Decided upon my grandmother's tea cosy.

Thursday 18 February

Sorting, tidying, cleaning, packing.

Friday 19 February

Went to the home of Rev William Charles Waldegrove-Smythe for a meal.

Arrived to see William Charles wearing a shirt and tie!

When I commented to him that I'd never seen him in one before, he said quickly that yes, yes, he had decided to take his cassock to be dry-cleaned. It would be ready tomorrow.

He took us into the drawing-room where his wife greeted us. She looked timid and small in comparison with her husband.

William Charles asked what I'd like to drink. Matthew answered for me, and started mocking my taste.

I interrupted with a glare towards Matthew, 'I do have my own mouth, thank you very much!'

William Charles regarded me with quiet disdain. 'Yes, you have, haven't you?' he said.

I was filled with regret that I had spoken in such a loud, coarse manner. I had come across as being extremely ill-bred.

All hopes of counterbalancing William Charles' suspicions of me were now dashed, and I had no one to blame but myself.

Saturday 20 February

Really looking forward to my birthday tomorrow. The children have gone to stay with friends for a night so Matthew and I will be on our own for a nice quiet celebration together.

Hope Matthew may give me some new perfume: I've hinted twice that mine's almost run out.

He hasn't said anything, so I guess he's planning a big surprise.

Sunday 21 February

My birthday.
Matthew forgot.
Slightly slower to forgive him than I like to confess.
Went to church with a fixed, Christian smile.
Sang, *May the fragrance of Jesus fill this place.*
I thought: Yes, but . . .

Tuesday 23 February

Shrove Tuesday. Made pancakes for the whole community, it seemed.

Talked with the children about whether it's a good idea to give things up for Lent.

Angus suggested he could give up tidying his room.

Philippa suggested I could give up getting cross.

Matthew told us we'd all got this Lent business entirely wrong. Said that, if we insisted on giving anything up, it should be feeling guilty.

'That,' he said, 'would be the best way of appreciating God's forgiveness. And it's a fat lot more appropriate during Lent than going without the odd bit of chocolate.'

Wednesday 24 February

Matthew bought me my birthday present. A deep blue vase with some lovely tulips, carved out of wood. They had been made in Bali. Beautiful.

I arranged them and put them in the lounge for all to see.

In the evening Rachel and her husband came round. They both immediately admired the flowers and didn't believe me at first when I said they were wooden.

'Take a closer look,' I said, picking one out of the vase. 'See—they come apart. The heads come off and then push back on.'

I passed it over. Rachel experimented, pulling off one head.

'Hey!' she exclaimed suddenly. 'This could make great psychotherapy. You could pretend that each tulip is a parishioner and take its head off!'

We all laughed.

'Um, can I come round and borrow them from time to time?' Rachel asked. Her voice sounded strangely pleading.

Thursday 25 February

Final meeting tonight of the group learning about Transactional Analysis.

Once or twice the discussion became a bit fraught. I looked over at Rachel. She was gazing most longingly at my carved wooden tulips. I wondered if she was wishing she could pull one out and take its head off. Or was it the whole bunch?

Sunday 28 February

Matthew's final service at the school—a service which Matthew started up in the hall there two years ago because there were no seats left in St. Mark's church. In any case, many people have been coming to this monthly family service who would never think of darkening the door of a church.

At the end of the service, after the blessing, Mrs Pinkerton stood up and gave a really warm thank you to Matthew and myself for everything. She itemised particular things which they appreciated about what Matthew had done, what we both mean to them.

I was very touched.

But what about all the people who are not moving? All the ones who keep plodding on, keep doing things, who continue to mean a lot to others—when will they be thanked?

It is a privilege to be appreciated.

March 1993

March 1993

Monday 1 March

Tired of sorting, tidying, cleaning and packing. Do NOT wish to do ANY more of it. EVER!

Unfortunately, this is the week we move!

Rachel phoned. She was giggling before she even began talking.

'Just got our copy of the church magazine,' she said. 'Have you seen it?'

'No.'

'Thought not. You should see what's in the diary for the Sunday after you leave . . . You must believe Luke, it's only coincidence that it falls on that date.'

Her voice held a question in it.

'OK,' I said. 'What's so special about the Sunday after we leave then?'

More giggles.

'It's Thanksgiving Sunday!' she said.

Maintained my composure. Did not reply.

Tuesday 2 March

More tired. Took up two carpets, with Matthew. Sifted and sorted through stuff which we've sifted and sorted through on the last four occasions we've moved house; stuff which we never use, which is junk, yet which we never want to part with.

'You just never know what that might come in handy for . . .' says Matthew every time.

I think I'm at the stage where I could take the whole lot to the rubbish tip. And I probably wouldn't mind throwing myself in at the same time: as long as I could get a bit of rest.

Wednesday 3 March

Exhausted and at the end of my tether.

Felt in too much need of tender, loving care to go to any house group meeting. I'd been invited to go and say an informal goodbye to the older ladies there. Had far too much to do. Every time I move any furniture I see cobwebs and a shameful amount of dust.

Decided I didn't have it in me to go and 'be nice'.

At the last minute, decided to pull the plug on all housework and go.

Was welcomed with such warmth, it was like balm. Fell into a chair where I sat like an exhausted wreck. Had coffee brought to me. They all showed so much interest in how I was, I told them. Including how fed up I was with cobwebs and bags.

Between them they worked out who could come and clean for me. Wouldn't even be thanked.

'Oh no, Jane! Just think, we can all gossip about you to our hearts' content and you'll never even know.'

They spoke with such a twinkle that I felt only accepted and loved. Wondered if we are total lunatics to leave this parish when there are people like these lovely ladies here.

Thanked them before I left. Thanked them for allowing me to be me, all the years here. Told them it was a gift.

They said, 'But it's normal, isn't it? To accept another person as they are?'

I said, 'Some parishes expect the Rector's wife to be a certain way, and they find it hard when she's not what they want.'

They nodded knowingly and hoped, with me, that that will not be the case in London.

But none of us knew for sure. That remains the great unknown.

Friday 5 March

Our last staff lunch together. Every week for years and years we've all met for lunch: the parish deacon, the minister Luke and Rachel his wife, Matthew and myself. We've taken it in turns to be hosts.

Today Rachel presented me with a gift. Beautifully wrapped.

'These are just for you, Jane,' she said. 'Nothing to do with parish gifts.'

I unwrapped the tissue paper to find several new carved wooden tulips whose heads could be pulled off and on again.

'I thought that, seeing as you'll be getting so many new parishioners, you might need more tulips to decapitate,' she explained. 'I'd hate you to run out.'

Evening An evening in which almost everyone in the parish at Runcorn turned out to make fun of the vicar. All in the name of saying goodbye to him.

They presented us with several presents, including (for Matthew) a glazier's trowel in memory of the 116 windows which he had replaced at Beersheba.

When we returned home, there was a note through the door from Annie—Annie who had been so weak with cancer, gradually regaining her strength but who could not face the evening with everyone.

Her letter was so moving, her thanks so sincere, it probably counted for more than all the presents.

'What we'll always treasure,' she wrote, 'is that we saw God in you, and you pointed us to Him.'

I prayed that that would be true not just of the vicar and his wife, but of every member of the church we were leaving.

Monday 8 March

Removal men arrived. They packed up our belongings and we moved house.

When it came to it, the process was remarkably simple.

Even through the tiredness and stress, we were aware of a tremendous excitement. We knew it was God who had guided us to our new home—through all those ups and downs; the false hopes and true disappointments. Knew we could trust Him that today's moving was His doing.

Thanked God for preparing us for our future. Asked Him to keep us loyal to our past. Trusted Him to sustain our hope.

And made lots of cups of tea for the removal men.

Postscript

June

Many, many listeners to Radio Merseyside have written to me since I stopped my weekly broadcasts. They say they *must* know what happened next.

After four months I can report that the new parish has survived me so far.

Only one nightmare has come true and I survived that.

I have never, ever sat in the Rectory Pew. In fact, the label was removed on the day before Matthew's first service.

Last weekend, over dinner, a parishioner observed, 'You know, you're quite right Jane. There are things that we wouldn't think of coping with ourselves, but which we expect you to handle just because you're the Rector's wife. Perhaps that is a *bit* unfair?'

I decided that progress had definitely been made in my campaign to show that, despite being a Rector's wife, I am normal.

Well, sometimes.

Post-Postscript

July

Went on holiday to France. We decided to camp, wanting to get as far Away From It All as possible. Chose the quietest site in the brochure.

First evening, went to find the loos and washing facilities. Entered a sort of hut thing: very clean, but rather shockingly open plan. Even by French standards, this was extremely exposed. There was no door into the Gents section and—accidentally of course—I found myself peering straight into the French *pissoire*.

A man was just finishing.

'*Pardon!*' I apologised breezily in my best French accent.

The man turned.

It was Rev William Charles Waldegrove-Smythe.